page 4

re	re	re	dis
over	over	de	de
dis	un	mis	mis

page 5

page 9

, , , ,

page 10

☑ ☑

☑ ☑

page 16

ent ant ent

ent ant ant

page 21

– how awful! – it was amazing!

– unbelievable! – I couldn't believe it!

page 23

hurried **led**

pleasant **colossal**

page 25

page 29

page 98

Finch   Kinsman   Hagarth   Randles

page 98   page 99

2 4 1 1 3 2 3 4   1000

page 100   100

£28 434   £12 895   £18 435   £14 750   10

page 110   3400

$\frac{5}{12}$ $\frac{2}{5}$ $\frac{1}{3}$ $\frac{1}{4}$ 340

$\frac{5}{8}$ $\frac{5}{12}$ 34

Well done!   Good job!   Clever me!

page 112

3 5 6 10

page 118

tariff 1   tariff 2   tariff 3   tariff 4   tariff 1   tariff 2   tariff 3   tariff 4

page 120

Clever me!

page 123

< < <

> > >

Well done!   Good job!

= > =

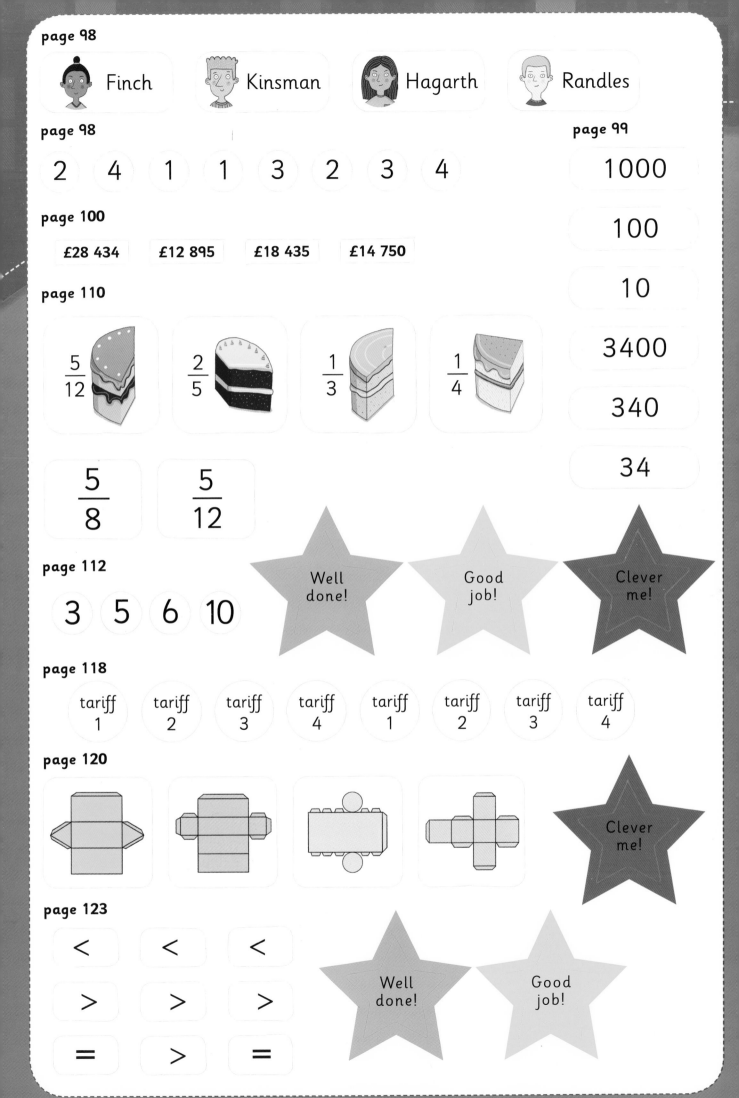

9-10 years

Leap Ahead

BUMPER

Workbook

Key Stage 2

ENGLISH

Home learning made FUN!

igloobooks

Better or best?

Make your noun phrases even better by improving your adjectives. Add *er* and *est* to show how something compares to other things around it. Complete the table below.

Root word	Add -er	Add -est
large	larger / longer	largest
long		
sharp	early	
pointy	Pointyter	tinyest
tiny		
rough		
smooth		
spiky		

Write two noun phrases about each alien on the dotted lines below using *er* and *est* adjectives. One has been done for you.

The pinkest alien with the roundest teeth...
....
....

....
....
....

2

Answers on page 32

Describing a monster!

Your monster has gone missing! You need to make a WANTED poster. Draw your monster in the box provided. Use exact descriptions of how he looks and how he acts or your monster may never be found!

WANTED

IF you find him watch out he might bite. He has two squiggly arms, three spiky horms, three big eyes, two huge fangs, and a large mouth. do not touch him, just phone 449 621 397

Prefix mix

Find prefixes on your sticker sheet and add them to the root words below to create new words. Remember not all prefixes work with every word.

(sticker) appear	(sticker) honest	(sticker) write
(sticker) heard	(sticker) read	(sticker) crowding
(sticker) spell	(sticker) cover	(sticker) frost
(sticker) think	(sticker) believe	(sticker) construct

Once you've correctly identified the new words above, find them in the word search below. Look horizontally, vertically and diagonally.

r	e	a	p	p	e	a	r	g	c	u	o
e	k	s	r	m	o	q	e	t	f	n	v
r	r	l	q	n	m	s	w	z	g	c	e
e	m	i	s	h	e	a	r	d	p	o	r
a	u	d	z	e	a	j	i	w	j	v	t
d	e	f	r	o	s	t	t	o	h	e	h
t	j	m	i	s	s	p	e	l	l	r	i
d	e	c	o	n	s	t	r	u	c	t	n
n	p	d	i	s	h	o	n	e	s	t	k
d	i	s	b	e	l	i	e	v	e	v	b
o	v	e	r	c	r	o	w	d	i	n	g

Answers on page 32

Homophones

Homophones are words that sound the same but are spelt differently, for example: *there/their/they're.*

For numbers 1 and 2 below, find and match a sticker from the sticker sheet to the correct homophone. Then, for each one, write a sentence using both homophones.

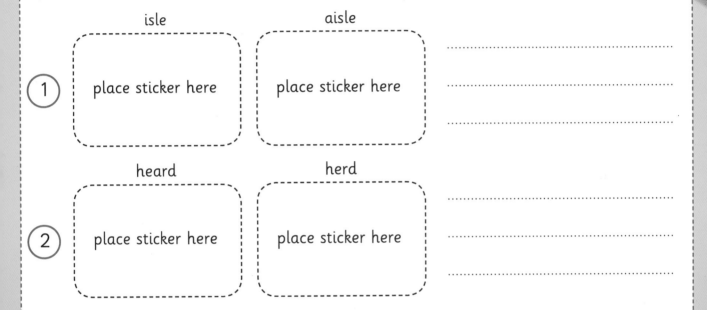

isle

place sticker here

aisle

place sticker here

① ....

....

....

heard

place sticker here

herd

place sticker here

② ....

....

....

For numbers 3 and 4 below, draw a picture to match the word. Then, for each one, write a sentence using both homophones.

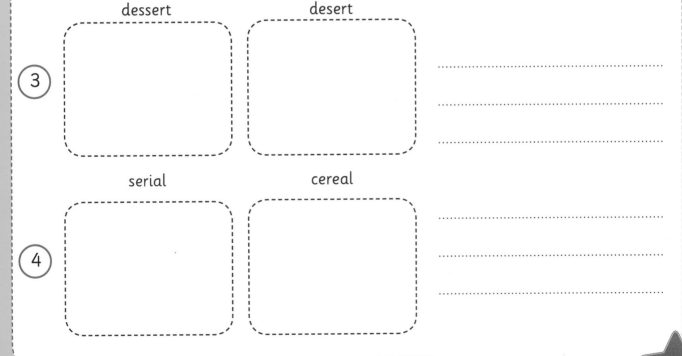

dessert

desert

③ ....

....

....

serial

cereal

④ ....

....

....

Answers on page 32

Fronted adverbials

Fronted adverbials help to link from one sentence to the next. They are also used to introduce paragraphs. Read the recount about a trip to the swimming pool. Find all the fronted adverbials in the text and underline each one.

On Saturday, a group of friends were taking a trip to the swimming pool. First, they got on the busy bus, which was full of passengers. On the bus, they chatted about what they were going to do at the pool. Everyone was so excited!

At last, they arrived. Right outside the pool, the bus ground to a halt. Finally, the four joyful friends hopped off. Inside, they queued for their tickets. Suddenly, they heard a groan. "Oh no! I've forgotten my trunks," shouted Ben from the back of the queue.

Sort the fronted adverbials into the table below. Add some more of your own, too.

Time	Place	Number

Answers on page 32

Dear Diary

Write a diary entry about a trip you have been on with your friends. Use fronted adverbials to link your sentences and introduce your paragraphs. To write an effective diary, imagine you are talking to your best friend. Give your opinion and talk about things you enjoyed or didn't like as well as writing what you have done. You might use questions and exclamations but remember not to use speech! After writing your diary entry, draw a picture in the box.

Relative clauses

Read the sentences below. Draw circles around the nouns.

The dog chased the pigeon.

One evening, Catherine caught the bus.

The friends loved going to the bowling alley.

The cat walked past the car.

The cyclist sped over the hill.

Answers on page 32

Relative clauses give more information about nouns. A relative clause starts with a relative pronoun (*who, which, when, where, that, whose*). A relative clause can be written about any of the nouns in the sentences you have just read.

For example:
The dog, <u>who was ferocious</u>, chased the pigeon.
The dog chased the pigeon, <u>which had a sore wing</u>.

Add relative clauses to the two sentences below. Choose an appropriate relative pronoun.

One night, Catherine, ...

...., caught the bus.

The friends loved going to the bowling alley, ...

....

8

A pair of commas

Read the sentences below. Notice where the relative clause goes. Look at the commas, which mark a relative clause when it is in the middle of a sentence.

Kayleigh loved her street dance lesson.

Kayleigh, who was a great dancer, loved her street dance lesson.

Can you add the commas in the following sentences? Use the comma stickers on the sticker sheet.

The house which was abandoned stood in the middle of the forest.

The giraffe when it ran looked gangly and clumsy.

Write three sentences of your own using relative clauses and commas.

....

....

....

....

....

....

....

Answers on page 32

Ending in *cial* or *tial*?

These two suffixes sound the same. Remember that *cial* is common after a vowel letter and *tial* is common after a consonant letter. There are some exceptions, such as: *financial, commercial, provincial* and *initial*.

Draw a link to match the beginnings of these words to the correct suffixes.

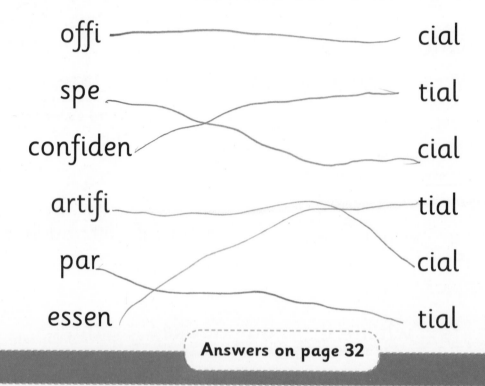

offi   cial

spe   tial

confiden   cial

artifi   tial

par   cial

essen   tial

Answers on page 32

Follow the rules (and the exceptions) to check which words below are spelt correctly. Cross out and change any incorrect spellings. Put a tick sticker next to correct spellings.

finantial   provintial   initial

benifitial   crucial   partial

confidencial   marcial   commercial

Answers on page 32

In the news

Look at what is happening in the pictures below. Write newspaper headlines for the disasters. Make sure your headlines have no more than 7 words. Choose the words carefully to attract the attention of the reader.

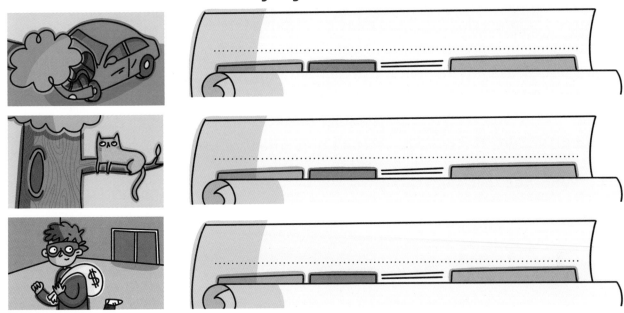

Read the newspaper report below.

On Thursday night, in the village of Greenton, a young couple narrowly escaped disaster. Severe winds of over 35 miles an hour had **got up** around the region. Some households reported losing roof tiles and several small trees had blown over in gardens. People were out in the wind **making safe** fences and bins.

After their dinner, Mr and Mrs Stone had set off in their car to check on Mrs Stone's parents. Around 6:30pm, they drove down Main Street when a sudden gust of wind uprooted a tree on the road side. The tree swayed and **shook** before falling down just in front of Mr and Mrs Stone's car, taking the bumper and number plate off. Luckily, the couple **answered** quickly, stopped the car and made a safe exit.

Evaluate whether the bold words in the report are correct for the situation. Look at the multiple choice selection below and put a ring around the one that makes the information in the report clear.

got up	built up	gathered	grown	developed
making safe	securing	fixing	pushing	sticking
shook	fell	creaked	leaned	trembled
answered	reacted	responded	jumped	went

A newspaper report

Read the report then record the main details by answering the questions.

On Saturday 1st May, Mrs Johnson reported her cat missing at the local police station in Bigtown. The police visited the area close to Mrs Johnson's house later that afternoon. Meowing was heard in the woods by two dog walkers. The police investigated and found little Fluffy (Mrs Johnson's cat) stuck up a large oak tree on the edge of the woods. With a little help from Stuart the builder and his ladder, the cat was rescued and safely returned to Mrs Johnson.

1. **Who has lost something?** ....

2. **What is missing?** ....

3. **When did she report it missing?** ....

4. **Where was it reported missing?** ....

5. **Why was it missing?** ....

....

Answers on page 32

Plan to write your own news report in a similar style to the ones you have read.

who	what	when	where	why

Use the details in the table to write your newspaper report. Think about how you will introduce it and make sure you write an ending to finish the report. Try writing expanded noun phrases and relative clauses to add extra details in your report to make it interesting for the reader.

PARENT TIP: Check your child writes the report in the past tense and uses the third person (*he, she, they, it*). They may want to add eyewitness accounts in direct or reported speech (e.g. *The couple said they were shocked and scared*).

Suffixes

You can turn many nouns and adjectives into verbs by adding the right suffix. Tick the boxes in the table below to choose the correct suffix, then write out the new verb.

Root word (adjective or noun)	-ate	-ise	-ify	Write out the new word (verb)
glory			√	glorify
elastic				
civil				
class				
active				
pure				
advert				
personal				

Do you notice any patterns when you add the suffix? Look closely at 'glory' and 'active'. What did you have to do?

....

....

....

Some of the words below are wrong. Can you cross out the incorrect ones and write the correct spelling above them?

personalify   civilise   advertate

activate   classify   glorise

Answers on page 32

PARENT TIP: Write out root words (e.g. *personal*, *civil* and *class*) on separate pieces of paper. Write out the suffixes *ise*, *ify* and *ate* on separate pieces of paper. Scatter them face-down on the table. Take turns to choose a word card and a suffix card. If they match, you get one point. If they don't match, put them face-down back on the table. The person with the most points after 5 minutes wins.

Correct commas

Add commas to the sentences in the correct places. You need to use commas to separate activities in a list, otherwise the meaning will be muddled! Can you imagine a kangaroo watching bounces or a snake dancing the twist?

The kangaroo watches bounces and hides in the bushes.

The python dances twists and turns.

The lion hunts shelters and lies in wait for prey.

Commas are also needed to mark the boundary between a main clause and a subordinate clause. Tick the sentences below that have commas in the correct place.

As the safari car drove through the jungle, the animals looked on.		As the safari car drove, through the jungle the animals looked on.	
As the chameleon watched the rain, it changed colour.		As the, chameleon watched the rain it changed colour.	
The zebra has black and white stripes, because it needs to camouflage from predators.		The zebra has black, and white stripes because it needs to camouflage from predators.	
Before the baby elephant could, move out the way the mother elephant squirted water over it!		Before the baby elephant could move out the way, the mother elephant squirted water over it!	

Answers on page 32

Competent spelling

These lily pads each have a root word which can end in the suffix *ent* or *ant*. The frog stickers on your sticker sheet have suffixes on them. Place each frog on the correct lily pad.

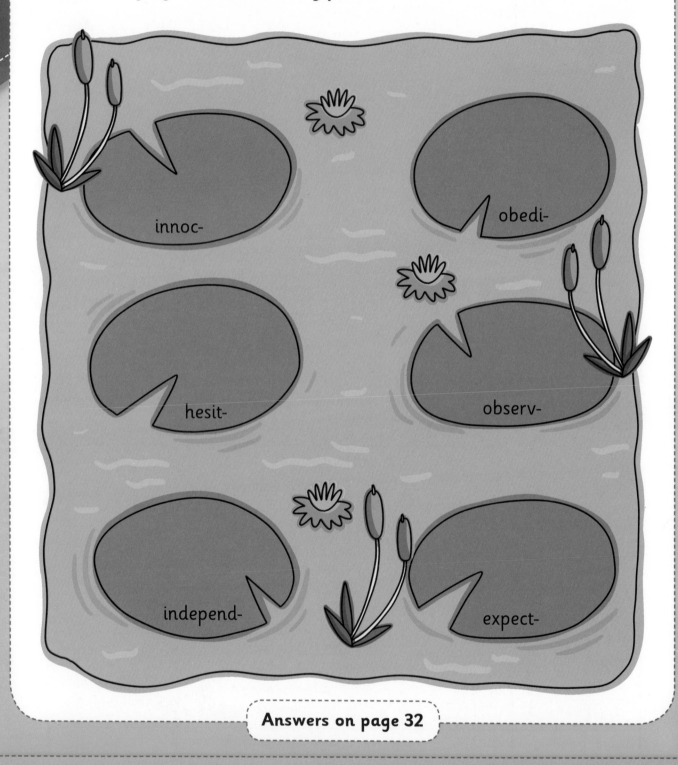

innoc-

obedi-

hesit-

observ-

independ-

expect-

Answers on page 32

PARENT TIP: Remind your child to choose *ent/ence/ency* following a soft *c*, *g* or *qu*. Choose *ant/ance/ancy* if there is a clear *a* sound as in *substance*. Remember that there are some exceptions.

Analysing a story

Predict what will happen in the story by looking at the three pictures below. Write your prediction on the dotted lines below, then read the story to see if you are correct.

....

....

Read the story below, then answer the questions.

Will had got a new game for his birthday. He hadn't opened it straight away as he was waiting to play it with his best friend, Sam. One evening, when Sam had come around for tea, the boys decided to open the dark and mysterious looking game. When they opened it, the boys were sure they heard a cannon firing in the distance. "That's odd!" thought Will. Once the box was opened, they quickly set up the game and Will rolled to go first. As he let go of the dice, the world began to spin. Both boys were lifted off the ground and the house turned to sky around them. Will could feel his heart beating loudly in his chest and questions were running through his mind. What had happened?

Suddenly, the sky settled. Sam and Will found themselves standing upright. The clouds and mist cleared away. At once, they both looked up and in front of them was a castle. Not just any castle – a castle that was at least twenty times bigger than them and had loud music coming from it! Sam looked over at his friend. "What should we do?" he asked.

Why didn't Will open the game straight away?

....

Find and copy the phrase in paragraph one that gives you a clue that there will be a castle in the game.

....

What was special about the castle?

....

Creating cohesion

You can use adverbials of time, place and manner to link across and within paragraphs of writing. Look at the adverbials below and draw a line from each one to the correct type.

firstly

finally
                                      place

in the afternoon

at dusk
                                      time

secondly
                                      number

around the corner

thirdly

Choose appropriate adverbials from the cloud to link the sentences in this paragraph together.

_____, the sky went black. _____, the thunder roared and the lightning filled every corner of the sky. _____, the friends took shelter from the storm. They weren't sure what to do next. "_____, we need to find somewhere safe and dry," thought one of them. _____, they set off, staying under the cover of the trees to find somewhere to sleep for the night.

firstly
suddenly
under the trees
a few minutes later
up above them

Answers on page 32

18

Planning a short story

Here are some ideas for characters and settings of a story.

Characters:	Settings:
An alien	Another planet
Two friends	A forest
A hooded figure	An abandoned school
A broken toy soldier	A castle
A knight	A shopping centre

Choose one character and one setting from the lists above, then decide on your own plot. Write sentences to describe your characters and setting. Try to use a mixture of short sentences and sentences joined with conjunctions. Can you use a relative clause?

Conjunctions:
because
when
after
while
as
but
and

characters are: Jim bob und mas.

Setting: an abonded Schoo

Weather: cold and rainy
day friday 1 June 1996

Which is your favourite sentence? Why?

Writing a short story

Write a short story (around 100 words) based on your plan on page 19.
Use the checklist below to make sure you include elements you've learnt about in this workbook.

Checklist:

☐ I've used adverbials for time.   ☐ I've used adverbials for place.

☐ I've used a range of conjunctions.   ☐ I've used simple sentences.

☐ I've used relative clauses.

It was a cold and rainy night in a zombie apocolypes 22 June Friday 1996 in a abonded school there was zombie teacher

Dashes

Dashes can be used to add comments and extra information at the end of a sentence. Use the stickers to add a comment or point of view to each of the main clauses below.

At the weekend, I went to a trampoline park with my friend ⌇ place sticker here ⌇

He collected a whole set of cards ⌇ place sticker here ⌇

The little girl fell ill on her birthday and missed her party ⌇ place sticker here ⌇

The boys broke the world record for an elastic band ball ⌇ place sticker here ⌇

Now write an email to a friend. Use dashes at the end of sentences to add extra information or a point of view.

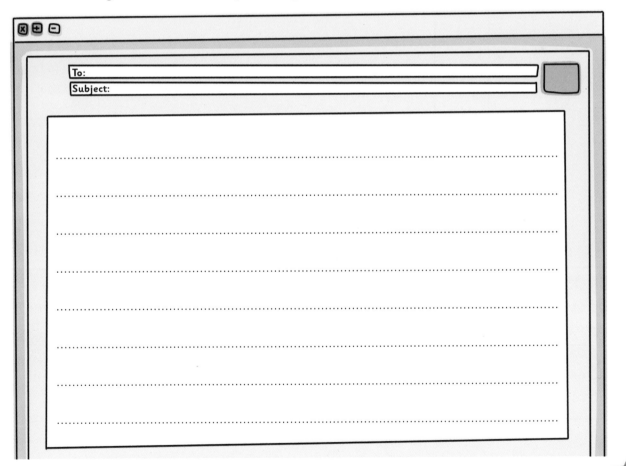

To:

Subject:

Silent letter crossword

All the answers to the clues have a silent letter in them. Find the answers to the clues and fill them into the crossword.

ACROSS

1 across: An upright cylindrical pillar which supports an arch or roof.

2 across: A landmass surrounded by water.

3 across: A feeling of uncertainty.

4 across: A piece of cutlery used for cutting.

DOWN

1 down: A man who serves a lord on horseback wearing armour.

2 down: A baby sheep.

3 down: Very serious and formal.

Answers on page 32

Choose the best word

Read the passage of writing below about a school trip to the museum. The writer has used some weak vocabulary (in bold). Select a sticker with a better word choice and stick it in place to improve the text.

Yesterday, Class 5 visited the city museum.

Firstly, the class got ready with coats, packed lunches and partners — everyone got to sit by their friend! When they arrived at the museum, they **went** excitedly to the front doors. The children were met by a **nice** museum assistant who showed them around all of the exhibits.

After that, the teacher **took** the class to the dinosaur gallery. They looked at the ichthyosaurs and plesiosaurs before finally spotting the **big** T-rex standing ahead of them. It was scary!

Read the next part of the text and look out for spelling, grammar and punctuation mistakes. Correct them with a coloured pen or pencil.

The next gallery they visited was full off stone tools. Everyone Enjoyed lucking at the flints and arrowheads.

At lunchtime, the class ate their packed lunches outside in the sunshine The museum had lots of picnic benchs for them to sit on whil they were eating their lunch

In the afternoon the class made observasions off the Ancient Greek artefacts. The vase paintings were very detailed. Their was so many jewels and objects to look at!

Answers on page 32

Exciting cities

Read these texts about two cities and then answer the questions about them.

New York city is in New York State (USA). Although it is a very well known city, it is not the capital city of America (Washington DC is). 8.4 million people live across the 5 boroughs of New York. These boroughs are called: Brooklyn, Bronx, Queens, Staten Island and Manhattan (which is the most visited borough). New York has several famous landmarks including the Statue of Liberty, which was a gift from France, situated on Liberty Island. Brooklyn Bridge, which connects Manhattan with Brooklyn, is one of the world's oldest suspension bridges. It opened in 1883.

Nairobi is the capital city of Kenya (a country situated in Eastern Africa). As well as having a busy metropolitan centre, the city has Nairobi National Park, which is a large game reserve known for breeding endangered black rhinos and home to giraffes, zebras and lions. Nairobi is the largest city between Cairo (Egypt) and Johannesburg (South Africa). Around 50 million people live in the country of Kenya, with just under 3 million people living in Nairobi. Nairobi is full of skyscrapers and world-class restaurants. Interestingly, Kenya's greatest export is tea!

1. **What is the capital city of America?** _Washington DC_

2. **How many boroughs are in New York City?** _5_

3. **Which borough has the most visitors?** _manhattan_

4. **What opened in 1883?** _Brooklyn bridge_

5. **How many more people live in New York than Nairobi?** _5.4 million_

6. **What makes Nairobi special?** _it's greatest export is tea_

7. **Where is Nairobi?** _kenya_

8. **Name 3 large cities in East Africa.** _Nairobi, Cairo and Johannesburg_

24

Answers on page 32

Parenthesis

You can leave out the relative pronoun in a relative clause when adding extra information if you add commas or brackets. This is called parenthesis and it sometimes makes a sentence easier to read. Look at the examples below.

Paris, **which is the capital city of France,** is in the north of the country.

Paris **(capital city of France)** is in the north of the country.

Paris, **the capital city of France,** is in the north of the country.

Put the stickers from the sticker sheet next to the correct sentences then write your own parentheses in these sentences.

| place sticker here | T-rex (...) lived in the Cretaceous period. |

| place sticker here | The local train (...) leaves at 2:30pm daily. |

| place sticker here | Trainers (...) are comfortable to wear when playing sport. |

| place sticker here | Swans (...) are extremely beautiful creatures. |

Using brackets

Draw four of your best friends in the boxes below. Describe your friends using brackets to add extra information.

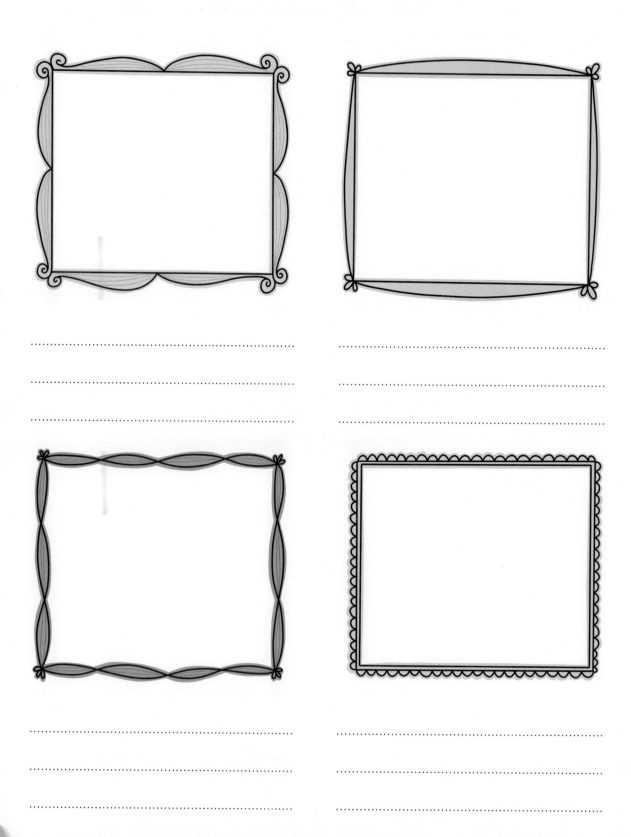

Paragraphs

As well as making sure each paragraph is linked to the next, you also need to link each sentence to the next so that your writing flows. You can use adverbs for this.

Read the sentences below. They are not in order. Your first job is to decide an order for them, then choose adverbs to link each one to the next. Write the sentences into a paragraph in your chosen order with adverbs (from the circle) to link them together.

Lions live in Africa in savannahs or grasslands.

A baby lion is called a cub and it will live up to 16 years in the wild.

Lions are large mammals belonging to the cat family.

They are very sociable animals and they live in groups called prides.

Female lions do most of the hunting while the male lions patrol to protect their territory.

furthermore
finally certainly
additionally
moreover firstly
also

....

....

....

....

....

....

....

....

Big spelling test

Can you spell all of these words? You have practised all the rules for them in this book. Ask an adult to test you or write out your spellings then check them yourself.

government

accommodate

appreciate

mischievous

especially

disastrous

opportunity

environment

profession

muscle

observation

knight

aisle

cereal

independence

hesitant

confidential

special

Sub-headings

Read each passage of text and write an appropriate sub-heading for each one, then a short introduction underneath the sub-heading to summarise what the paragraph is about. Finally, find a sticker that matches the topic, stick it in the box and write a caption underneath it.

....

....

Many people believe children in Year 5 should not have mobile phones because they may lose them or smash them. Teachers think it is unfair for some children to own phones and not others. Some parents think it is hard to manage ten year olds on social media. However, Year 5 children feel they are useful for keeping in contact, especially when they walk home on their own.

place sticker here

....

....

....

Cricket is a game played by people of all ages. The game involves two teams (a batting team and a bowling team). The game requires several pieces of equipment: bats, a hard ball and stumps with bails placed on top. It is played on a large, circular field. The team that scores the most runs is the winner.

place sticker here

....

....

....

There are many different types of ride at theme parks including rollercoasters and water rides. Theme parks are enjoyed by all members of the family, not just for the rides but for the surroundings, gardens and food. Visiting theme parks can be expensive but also a great deal of fun.

place sticker here

....

My fact file

You have been asked to create a guide about an animal found in the jungle. Plan out an informative report on a jungle animal of your choice.

The questions below will help you plan your guide. Plan each paragraph using the boxes below.

What does the creature look like?
Where does it live?
What does it eat?
What does the creature do during the day?
What does the creature do during the night?
Do you have an interesting fact to end?

Subheading	
Notes	

Subheading	
Notes	

Subheading	
Notes	

Now it's time to write your report. Remember to include: sub-headings for each paragraph, adverbs for cohesion, relative clauses, brackets, dashes and commas. Draw a picture of the animal in the empty box.

Answers

Page 2: Better or best?
large/larger/largest; long/longer/longest; sharp/sharper/sharpest; pointy/pointier/pointiest; tiny/tinier/tiniest; rough/rougher/roughest; smooth/smoother/smoothest; spiky/spikier/spikiest

Page 4: Prefix mix
reappear, misheard, misspell, overthink, dishonest, reread, uncover, disbelieve, rewrite, overcrowding, defrost, deconstruct

r	e	a	p	p	e	a	r	g	c	u	o
e	k	s	r	m	o	q	e	t	f	n	v
r	r	l	q	n	m	s	w	z	g	c	e
e	m	i	s	h	e	a	r	d	p	o	r
a	u	d	z	e	a	j	i	w	j	v	t
d	e	f	r	o	s	t	t	o	h	e	h
t	j	m	i	s	s	p	e	l	l	r	i
d	e	c	o	n	s	t	r	u	c	t	n
n	p	d	i	s	h	o	n	e	s	t	k
d	i	s	b	e	l	i	e	v	e	v	b
o	v	e	r	c	r	o	w	d	i	n	g

Page 5: Homophones
1. isle = island sticker / aisle = shopping aisle sticker
2. heard = ear sticker / herd = group of cows sticker
3. dessert = e.g. a sweet treat eaten after dinner / desert = e.g. a vast dry land
4. serial = e.g. a series of TV shows or books / cereal = e.g. a bowl of food eaten for breakfast

Page 6: Fronted adverbials
Time: On Saturday / At last / Suddenly
Place: On the bus / Right outside the pool / Inside
Number: First / Finally

Page 8: Relative clauses
Nouns: dog / pigeon / Catherine / bus / friends / bowling alley / cat / car / cyclist / hill

Page 9: A pair of commas
The house, which was abandoned, stood in the middle of the forest.
The giraffe, when it ran, looked gangly and clumsy.

Page 10: Ending in *cial* or *tial*?
official / special / confidential / artificial / partial / essential
Correct: initial / crucial / partial / commercial
Incorrect: finantial / provintial / benifitial / confidencial / marcial

Page 12: A newspaper report
1. Mrs Johnson. **2.** Her cat. **3.** Saturday 1st May. **4.** The local police station. **5.** It was stuck up a large oak tree.

Page 14: Suffixes
glory / -ify / glorify; elastic / -ate / elasticate; civil / -ise / civilise; class / -ify / classify; active / -ate / activate; pure / -ify / purify; advert / -ise / advertise; personal / -ise / personalise

Page 15: Correct commas
The kangaroo watches, bounces and hides in the bushes.
The python dances, twists and turns.
The lion hunts, shelters and lies in wait for prey.

As the safari car drove through the jungle, the animals looked on.	√	As the safari car drove, through the jungle the animals looked on.	
As the chameleon watched the rain, it changed colour.	√	As the, chameleon watched the rain it changed colour.	
The zebra has black and white stripes, because it needs to camouflage from predators.		The zebra has black, and white stripes because it needs to camouflage from predators.	√
Before the baby elephant could, move out the way the mother elephant squirted water over it!		Before the baby elephant could move out the way, the mother elephant squirted water over it!	√

Page 16: Competent spelling
innocent / obedient / hesitant / independent / expectant / observant

Page 18: Creating cohesion
Place: around the corner / **Time:** in the afternoon, at dusk / **Number:** firstly, secondly, thirdly, finally

There are several appropriate answers for this activity. One example is below:
Suddenly, the sky went black. Up above them, the thunder roared and the lightning filled every corner of the sky. Under the trees, the friends took shelter from the storm. They weren't sure what to do next. "Firstly, we need to find somewhere safe and dry," thought one of the friends. A few minutes later, they set off, staying under the cover of the trees to find somewhere to sleep for the night.

Page 22: Silent letter crossword
1 down: knight / 2 down: lamb / 3 down: solemn / 1 across: column / 2 across: island / 3 across: doubt / 4 across: knife

Page 23: Choose the best word
went = hurried / nice = pleasant / took = led / big = colossal

The next gallery they visited was full **of** stone tools. Everyone enjoyed **looking** at the flints and arrowheads. At lunchtime, the class ate their packed lunches outside in the sunshine. The museum had lots of picnic **benches** for them to sit on **while** they were eating their lunch. In the afternoon, the class made **observations of** the Ancient Greek artefacts. The vase paintings were very detailed. **There were** so many jewels and objects to look at!

Page 24: Exciting cities
1. Washington DC
2. 5
3. Manhattan
4. Brooklyn Bridge
5. 5.4 million
6. It has a National Park. It has skyscrapers. It has world-class restaurants.
7. Kenya
8. Nairobi, Cairo, Johannesburg

9-10 years

Leap Ahead
BUMPER
Workbook

Key Stage 2

MATHS

Home learning made FUN!

Big numbers

Jamie's family are thinking of moving house and have narrowed their search down to these houses.

 £260 745
 £225 985
 £209 459
 £229 995

Jamie reads the first price as "twenty-six thousand seven hundred and forty-five pounds". Can you correct his mistake?

Two hundred and Sixty thousand Seven hundred and 45

Write the prices of the other houses in words.

2 £225 985 — two hundred and twenty five thousand nine hundred and Eighty five

3 £209 459 — two hundred and nine thousand sour hundred and Sixty nine

4 £229 995 — two hundred and twenty nine thousand nine hundred and Ninety six

Jamie wants to compare the prices. Use the stickers to put the prices in order from lowest to highest.

£209 459   £225 985   £229 995   £260 745

Lowest ——————————————————→ Highest

A week later, the houses have been reduced in price. Can you write how much each house was reduced by?

1  £244 745   16,000

2  £217 985   8,000

3  £189 459   20,000

4  £227 995   2,000

Answers on page 64

Decimal numbers

The family are considering how close each house is to the local school. The distances in kilometres are written on the map.

Jamie says that house 2 is closest because it has the fewest decimal places. Mum says this isn't true. Can you explain to Jamie why?

Use stickers to put the houses in order of their distance from the school.

2.015 km

2.05 km

2.5 km

2.155 km

Closest ⟶ Furthest

Jamie then works out how far each house is from his friend's house. Circle the one that is closest.

1.

4.05 km

2.

5.4 km

3.

4.445 km

4.

5.55 km

Answers on page 64

PARENT TIP: Write some whole numbers up to 1 million or some decimal numbers with up to 3 decimal places on pieces of paper. Turn them over in a pile. Play "Higher or lower", taking turns to guess whether the next number turned over will be higher or lower than the last.

Multiplying and dividing by 10, 100 and 1000

Callum is working at a pop concert, checking fans' tickets at the door.

1000 fans come through each of the 23 doors. How many fans are at the concert altogether?

....

Later, Callum sells merchandise. Mugs come in boxes of 10, T-shirts come in boxes of 100 and keyrings come in boxes of 1000. Callum works out how many of each he's sold by multiplying the number of boxes he opened by the number in a box. Complete his calculations for him below.

How many mugs in 342 boxes?

3 4 2 x 1 0 = ...

How many boxes makes 7500 keyrings?

.... x 1 0 0 0 = 7 5 0 0

How many boxes has Callum opened when he's sold 2400 T-shirts?

1 0 0 x .... = ...

He also sells 3000 programmes from 30 boxes. How many programmes come in a box?

.... x 3 0 = 3 0 0 0

The next night, Callum helps in the food kiosk. He wants to know how much money the concert makes for every 10, 100 and 1000 items sold. He makes a table to record his workings. Can you help him complete it?

	x1	x10	x100	x1000
Fizzy drinks	£1.99		£199	
Portion of chips	£2.30	£23		
Burgers				£3500
Popcorn	£2.05			
Chocolate bars			£95	

Answers on page 64

Callum is wondering how to measure different items around the kiosk. What unit of measure would he use to measure the following items? Use stickers to match them with the correct unit.

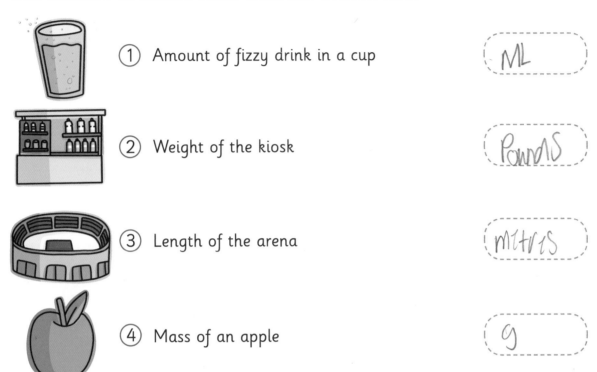

① Amount of fizzy drink in a cup — ML

② Weight of the kiosk — Powds

③ Length of the arena — metres

④ Mass of an apple — g

These are the weights of some of the refreshments. Put them in order from lightest to heaviest using the stickers on the sticker sheet.

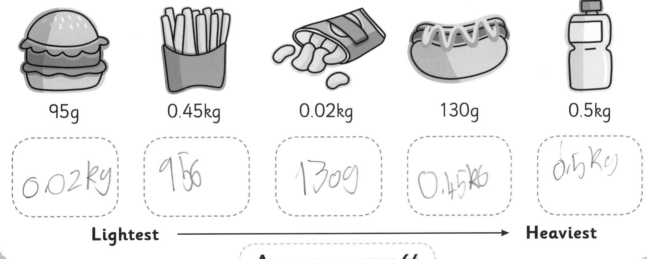

| 95g | 0.45kg | 0.02kg | 130g | 0.5kg |

| 0.02kg | 95g | 130g | 0.45kg | 0.5kg |

Lightest ———————————————→ Heaviest

Answers on page 64

PARENT TIP: Give your child regular opportunities to familiarise themselves with measures in everyday life. While cooking, let them weigh ingredients and convert the measures to bigger or smaller units. When measuring to redecorate, let them use the tape measure and tell you the measurement in more than one way, for example 3.4m or 340cm.

Rounding whole numbers

Here is a table showing the number of fans for different teams watching a big football match on television. Round each of the first 3 teams' fans to complete the table.

Team	Fans	Nearest 1000	Nearest 10 000	Nearest 100 000
1	162 739			
2	250 182			
3	306 873			
4		224 000	220 000	200 000
5		178 000	180 000	200 000

(a) What could the number of fans be for the fourth team? Give 3 answers.

....

(b) Lily says that the smallest number of fans that team 5 could have is 178 001. Do you agree? Give a reason for your answer.

....

....

(c) When rounded to the nearest thousand, Team 6 rounds to 24 000 fans. Team 7 has 1 more fan and rounds to 25 000 fans. How many fans does each team have?

Team 6: ....   Team 7: ....

Answers on page 64

Lucy and Rory are going to watch a football match live. They go online to work out how much money they will need to spend.

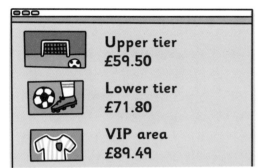

Upper tier
£59.50

Lower tier
£71.80

VIP area
£89.49

(d) Lucy chooses the ticket she wants and says it's about £72. Which ticket has she chosen?

....

(e) Rory wants to go to the VIP area. How much are these tickets to the nearest pound?

....

(f) They decide on VIP tickets. Lucy estimates the cost for two tickets as £180. Rory estimates it will be £178. How did they get different estimates?

....

Home kit
£26.75

Away kit
£24.95

Training kit
£18.25

Beanie hat
£?

Socks
£18.25

(g) They look online to buy some merchandise for the match. Lucy says an away kit is about £20 but Rory says it is about £30. Who is correct and why?

....

....

(h) Lucy rounds the price of a hat to £23 to the nearest pound. What is the largest and smallest amount it might cost?

....

(i) Rory's dad tells him he can buy a souvenir with a price that rounds to £25. What can Rory buy?

....

Answers on page 64

PARENT TIP: Think of a number with up to 6 digits. For example, 371 348. Give your child clues, e.g. "My number rounds to 370 000 when rounded to the nearest 10 000. It rounds to 400 000 to the nearest 100 000. It rounds to 371 300 to the nearest 100". Can they guess your number? Try it for decimals using wholes, tenths and hundredths too.

Adding and subtracting mentally

Ben's mum and dad want to buy a few new electrical items. They ask Ben to work out the total costs of different combinations but he has no pen and paper so will need to do it mentally.

Can you use the stickers to show which strategy would be most efficient for each of the combinations?

£224 + £228

£532 + £1425

£416 + £532 + £224

£1425 + £199

(a) Ben likes a television that costs £2345 but mum and dad prefer one costing £1999. How much more does Ben's cost? Use jottings to show how you could do it mentally.

(b) Ben's parents have £3000 to spend. If they buy a television for £1400, a tablet for £350 and a games console costing £175, how much would they have left?

(c) They decide on a television costing £1465, a dvd player costing £270, a games console for £335 and two spare remotes each costing £15. What's the best order to add these prices? Show your jottings.

Answers on page 64

Adding and subtracting with written methods

The electrical store isn't making as much money now that online sales have increased, so Tim the manager is comparing the profits to the same time last year.

	Profit (£) last year	Profit (£) this year
January	239 962	182 045
February	161 528	94 387
March	97 037	87 238

Help Tim to work out the difference in profit for each of the first 3 months of the year.

January

```
  239 962
-182 045
_____


_____
```

February

```
 161 528
- 94 387
_____


_____
```

March

```
 97 037
-87 238
_____


_____
```

In which month were profits down the most? ....

Tim estimates that last year, the store made approximately £500 000 in the first 3 months, while this year it made only £360 000. How do you think he worked out these estimations?

....

Tim works out the total profit for the first 3 months of last year and compare it to this year. Complete his calculations for him.

```
  239 962
  161 528
+  97 037
_____


_____
```

```
  182 085
   94 387
+  87 238
_____


_____
```

Answers on page 64

Multiples

Shoulder: 3 points
Back: 4 points
Front: 5 points

Tom and his friends are playing Laser Tag. Tom always aims for the shoulders so his score goes up in multiples of 3. Finlay shoots his opponents' backs so his score adds on 4 each time.

Which scores on the sticker sheet could have been seen on Tom and Finlay's packs during the game? Sort them into the Venn diagram.

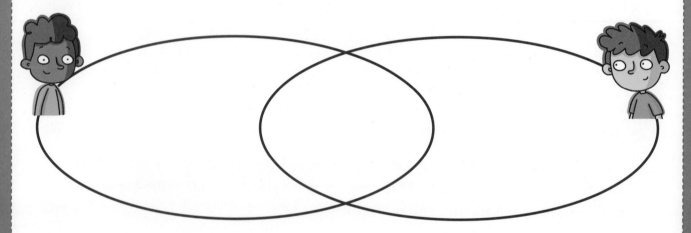

(a) Which scores will they both have at some point in the game? What do you notice about the scores?

....

(b) What will be the next three scores they have in common?

....

(c) Tom shoots three sets of shoulders. His score is 3 × 3 = 9. Finlay shoots four backs and has scored 4 × 4 = 16. Fran, who always shoots fronts, has scored 5 × 5 = 25 after five shots. Fran says these are special numbers but can't remember what they are called. Can you?

....

(d) Give Fran three more examples of these numbers.

....

(e) Finlay says he knows some more special numbers called cube numbers. One is 2 × 2 × 2 = 8. Can you find the next three cube numbers?

....

Later, they go for milkshakes and chat about the scoring system. They think there should be more ways to score points. They decide **on new scores:** Arms: 6 points, Upper legs: 7 points, Lower legs: 8 points, Hands: 9 points.

They play a game of *Guess our Target* using their new score system. The children each have a different target but fire the same number of shots. Can you guess the body parts each child is thinking of and work out how many shots they took?

(f) I scored 49 and Fran scored 56.

(g) I scored 84 and Finlay scored 108.

(h) I scored 48 and Tom scored 72.

....

(i) Tom says that if they shoot more than one person, there are some scores that aren't possible like 3, 5 and 17. He thinks this is because they are odd numbers. Do you agree?

....

(j) Can you think of three more scores between 5 and 30 that aren't possible?

....

Multiplying mentally

Poppy works at the cinema. She works on the refreshment kiosk on Friday night. The computer systems aren't working so she must work out all the costs mentally. Can you help her?

(a) $85p \times 4 =$ .... (use doubling to help you)

(b) $£3.50 \times 14 =$ .... (double one and half the other)

(c) $£3.40 \times 5 =$ .... (multiply by 10 and halve the answer)

On Saturday, Poppy is selling tickets. Children's tickets are £9 each and adults' are £13. For each question, circle your choice and find the total.

(d) 8 adults pay for their tickets together. Poppy can't remember her 8 times table. How could she find the answer to £13 × 8?

$13 \times 4 \times 4$ $13 \times 4 \times 2$ $13 \times 4 + 2$

(e) 23 children at a party buy tickets for a film. Poppy starts working out the total price by doing 23 × 10 but she isn't sure how to adjust the answer. What should she do?

$23 \times 10 - 1$ $23 \times 10 - 23$ $23 \times 10 - 9$

(f) 12 seniors arrive. They pay £7 for their tickets. Holly doesn't know the answer to 7 × 12. Which of these calculations would not give her the answer? Can you explain why?

$12 \times 5 + 12 \times 2$ $10 \times 7 + 2 \times 7$ $11 \times 7 + 11$

Answers on page 64

The cinema has some special promotions on.

TICKET PRICES

ADULT: £13	FAMILY: £35	COUPLE: £24
CHILD: £9	SENIOR: £7	

Poppy is curious about which types of tickets make the most money so she multiplies the number of each ticket sold this week by its price.

g £13 × 30 = ...

h £9 × 45 = ...

i £35 × 4 = ...

j £7 × 25 = ...

k £24 × 11 = ...

Which ticket type makes the most money?

....

The week after, Poppy does the same again but she makes some mistakes. Can you tell her what she has done wrong?

l £13 × 8 = 13 × 2 × 2 × 2 × 2 = £208

....

m £9 × 13 = 9 × 12 + 13 = £109

....

n £24 × 0 = £24

....

Dividing mentally

Martha works at the travel agents in the currency exchange. Today she is exchanging foreign currency back to British pounds for customers who didn't spend all the money they took on holiday.

These are the current exchange rates for different currencies per pound:

5 Turkish Lira	7 Ghanian Cedi
2 Australian Dollar	12 Swedish Krona
4 Brazilian Real	8 Croatian Kuna
6 Saudi Arabian Real	11 Hong Kong Dollars
9 Danish Krone	3 Barbadian Dollars

Martha knows she needs to divide the customers' amounts by the conversion rate (currency per pound). She is trying to use the best method for each conversion. Can you use her method to convert each amount?

a

"I have 148 Brazilian Real left."

Martha says the best way to divide by 4 is to halve and halve again.

Workings:

Answer: ....

b

"I have 230 Turkish Lira left."

Martha says the best way to divide by 5 is to divide by 10 and double the answer.

Workings:

Answer: ....

c

"I have 630 Ghanaian Cedi left."

Martha says she can use the fact that $63 \div 7 = 9$ to work this out.

Workings:

Answer: ....

Answers on page 64

Dividing with written methods

For these exchanges, Martha cannot find a good mental strategy so she uses a written method. Can you complete her calculations?

a "I have 495 Danish Krone left."

$$9 \overline{\smash{)}495}$$

b "I have 357 Brazilian Real left."

$$4 \overline{\smash{)}357}$$

c "I have 452 Croatian Kuna left."

$$8 \overline{\smash{)}452}$$

d "I have 1029 Saudi Arabian Real left."

$$6 \overline{\smash{)}1029}$$

Martha's pen has leaked on these calculations. Can you work out what the missing digits might be? Use the stickers on the sticker sheet to cover over the pen splodges.

$$3 \overline{\smash{)}4\ 9\ \blacksquare}} \quad 1\ \blacksquare\ 5$$

$$\blacksquare \overline{\smash{)}6\ 2\ 0} \quad 1\ 2\ \blacksquare$$

$$7 \overline{\smash{)}9\ \blacksquare\ 7} \quad 1\ 3\ \blacksquare$$

Answers on page 64

PARENT TIP: Give children division calculations with 3 or 4 digit numbers. Ask them to decide between a mental or written method. Encourage them to use a mental calculation first. Can they see any multiplication facts within the numbers? Can they use halving?

Ordering fractions

Lucy and her friends are having a sleepover at her house and all their parents have sent food for them to share.

Lucy has already eaten $\frac{1}{3}$ of her popcorn. Kirsty has eaten $\frac{2}{9}$ of hers. Who has eaten the most? Use equivalent fractions to prove it.

Compare these other amounts that each child has enjoyed by inserting the correct symbol from the sticker sheet.

a  $\frac{3}{4}$ ☐ $\frac{5}{8}$ b  $\frac{3}{5}$ ☐ $\frac{11}{15}$

c  $\frac{3}{4}$ ☐ $\frac{7}{10}$ d  $\frac{3}{4}$ ☐ $\frac{7}{12}$

Here are some more fractions separated by a symbol. Can you fill in the missing numerators and denominators?

 $\frac{3}{10} > \frac{}{5}$ $\frac{3}{4} < \frac{}{8}$

 $\frac{2}{3} > \frac{}{6}$ $\frac{1}{4} > \frac{1}{}$

Answers on page 64

There are treats left over so the children combine them to keep for next time. Hannah and Francesca combine their snacks together. They have $1\frac{1}{4}$ boxes of popcorn. Hannah says this is $\frac{5}{4}$ because there are 4 quarters in a whole box plus the quarter left over. Can you convert their other amounts into improper fractions?

 $2\frac{1}{3} = \frac{}{3}$

$5\frac{1}{2} = \frac{}{2}$

 $1\frac{5}{8} = \frac{}{8}$

$3\frac{3}{4} = \frac{}{4}$

Lucy combines her leftovers with Alice and Jasmine. Kirsty combines hers with Sophie and Amira. Which group has the most left over? Insert the correct symbol from the sticker sheet.

a

Lucy's group   Kirsty's group

$2\frac{1}{4}$ ⬚ $\frac{7}{4}$

b

Lucy's group   Kirsty's group

$2\frac{1}{5}$ ⬚ $\frac{12}{5}$

c

Lucy's group   Kirsty's group

$\frac{11}{8}$ ⬚ $1\frac{5}{8}$

d

Lucy's group   Kirsty's group

$2\frac{14}{3}$ ⬚ $5\frac{1}{3}$

The two groups combine their leftover pizza and ice cream. How much do they have in total?

 $2\frac{1}{4} + \frac{7}{4} =$

 $2\frac{1}{5} + \frac{12}{5} =$

Answers on page 64

PARENT TIP: Cut up food into equal parts so your child can see how the parts relate to each other, e.g. a cake cut into thirds has half as many pieces as a cake cut into sixths. Can they compare $\frac{2}{3}$ to $\frac{5}{6}$, using equivalent fractions to change thirds into sixths? Then they can add $\frac{2}{3}$ of one cake to $\frac{5}{6}$ of another and work out how much they have in total.

49

Adding and subtracting fractions

Sean and Robin have been washing the neighbours' cars over the summer holidays. At the end of each day, they measure how much detergent they each have left in their bottles. Can you use equivalent fractions to work out how much they have left in total? The first one has been done for you.

	Sean	Robin	Total
Monday	$\frac{1}{5}$	$\frac{7}{10}$	$\frac{1}{5} + \frac{7}{10} = \frac{2}{10} + \frac{7}{10} = \frac{9}{10}$
Tuesday	$\frac{3}{4}$	$\frac{3}{12}$	
Wednesday	$\frac{1}{2}$	$\frac{2}{5}$	
Thursday	$\frac{2}{3}$	$\frac{1}{5}$	
Friday	$\frac{1}{6}$	$\frac{3}{8}$	

The following week, they use up some of the leftovers. They subtract how much they used each day from how much was in the bottle at the start of the day, then cancel the fraction to its simplest form. How much do they have left each day? The first one has been done for you.

	Amount at start of day	Amount at end of day	Total
Monday	$\frac{3}{4}$	$\frac{5}{8}$	$\frac{3}{4} - \frac{5}{8} = \frac{6}{8} - \frac{5}{8} = \frac{1}{8}$
Tuesday	$1\frac{1}{5}$	$\frac{7}{10}$	
Wednesday	$1\frac{1}{3}$	$\frac{5}{12}$	
Thursday	$1\frac{1}{6}$	$\frac{3}{4}$	
Friday	$1\frac{2}{3}$	$\frac{3}{5}$	

Answers on page 64

At the end of the summer, they have a lot of bottles with different amounts of detergent left inside. They sort them into piles of the same fraction. Can you use these diagrams to help you work out how much is left altogether? Show your workings.

(a)

$\dfrac{2}{3} \times 3 =$ ....

(b)

....

....

....

(c)

....

....

....

(d)

....

....

....

Answers on page 64

PARENT TIP: Give children real objects that can be broken into fractions and ask them to multiply them by a whole number. Repeatedly add the same amount. Only the numerator (top part of the fraction) is multiplied (e.g. $\frac{2}{3}$ of a cake x 4 = $\frac{8}{3}$ or $2\frac{2}{3}$).

Percentages

Sadie and her two friends all have tablets but they notice their battery indicators show the power remaining in different ways. Ethan's red tablet shows a fraction. Vicki's blue tablet shows a decimal. Sadie's yellow tablet shows a percentage.

Using the stickers on the sticker sheet, put their tablets into groups where they all show the same battery power. One group has been done for you.

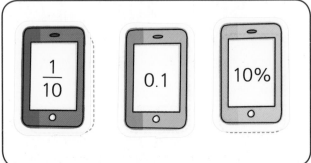

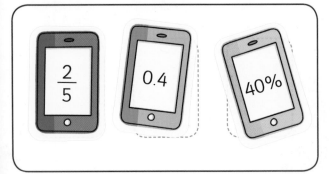

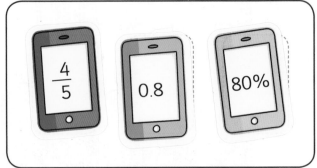

Put these battery indicators in order from lowest power to highest.

$$30\% \qquad 0.6 \qquad \frac{8}{10} \qquad 0.25 \qquad \frac{1}{25}$$

....

Answers on page 64

(a) Ethan has used $\frac{7}{10}$ of his battery power. What percentage has he got left?

....

(b) Vicki's tablet shows 0.2 remaining. What fraction would Ethan's show? Write the fraction in its simplest form.

....

(c) Sadie's tablet shows 60% remaining. How much power has she used? Give the answer as a decimal.

....

(d) Ethan has $\frac{3}{10}$ left. Sadie has 35%. Who has the most and by how much?

....

....

(e) Vicki has 0.45 left and Sadie has 30%. How much more has Vicki got? Give the answer as a fraction in its simplest form.

....

....

(f) Ethan has $\frac{2}{5}$ left. Sadie has 10% more. What does her display show?

....

Answers on page 64

Answers on page 64

PARENT TIP: Play 'percentage patience'. Write these fractions, percentages and decimals on small pieces of card: 0.5, 50%, $\frac{3}{10}$, 0.3, $\frac{1}{4}$, 0.25, $\frac{7}{10}$, 70%, 40%, 4%, $\frac{3}{5}$, 0.6. Place them upside down spread over a table. Take turns with your child to turn them over, 2 at a time. The aim is to find a matching pair. When you do, keep both cards. If they don't match, turn them upside down again.

53

Shapes

Karl has been learning about shapes at school but struggles to remember all their properties. He has downloaded an app to help him. He has to decide if the shape is regular or irregular. Can you help him? Use the regular and irregular polygons on your sticker sheet and place them in the correct side of the table below.

Regular polygons	Irregular polygons

(a) Karl thinks this triangle is regular because it has two equal sides. Do you agree? Explain why.

....

....

(b) Karl thinks this rectangle is regular because it has equal angles. Do you agree? Explain why.

....

....

(c) Can you give Karl two rules to check any polygon is regular?

....

....

Answers on page 64

Karl's app asks him to identify 3D shapes from their properties. Use the properties to work out the name of the shape from the list below, then fill in the vertices and edges. Finally, add a sticker of the shape. *Shape names: hexagonal prism, triangular prism, cuboid, square-based pyramid, triangular-based pyramid, cylinder.*

6 rectangular faces
2 hexagonal faces

☐ vertices

☐ edges

⬚

1 square face
4 triangular faces

☐ vertices

☐ edges

⬚

3 rectangular faces
2 triangular faces

☐ vertices

☐ edges

⬚

2 circular faces
1 curved face

☐ vertices

☐ edges

⬚

6 rectangular faces
3 pairs of equal faces

☐ vertices

☐ edges

⬚

4 triangular faces

☐ vertices

☐ edges

⬚

Answers on page 64

PARENT TIP: Ask your child to identify shapes around them (2D and 3D). Where do we see prisms? For example, on food packaging – go to the supermarket and see how many prism-shaped boxes you can find. Why is a cuboid such a useful shape?

55

Angles

On their residential trip, the children from Year 5 are orienteering. The teacher starts the groups off two at a time from the side of the building and they head off in two different directions. Complete the missing angle in each diagram.

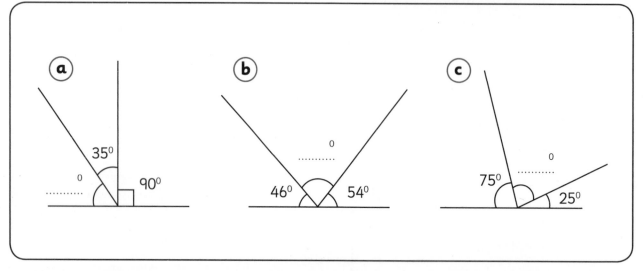

a   35⁰   0 ....   90⁰

b   0 ....   46⁰   54⁰

c   75⁰   0 ....   25⁰

Jess and Natalie finish early so they play a game. Their teacher calls out instructions at random. The first to face the start again wins. Here are the instructions they each follow, turning clockwise each time:

Jess	Natalie
quarter turn	half turn
half turn	three quarter turn
2 half turns	half turn
three quarter turn	one and a half turns
quarter turn	quarter turn
one and a half turns	one and a half turns
three quarter turn	quarter turn

Who will face the start again first?

The children in Ali's group always seem to disagree on which direction they should walk. Mark the missing angles on each diagram to show the angle that Ali, Ben and Chris each turn from one another.

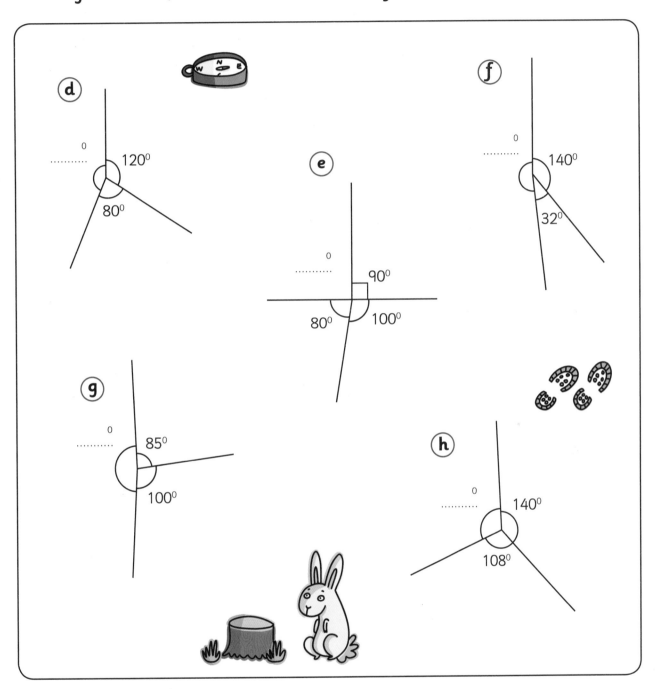

Answers on page 64

PARENT TIP: Play games that involve turning to quarter, half, three quarter and full turns, like Jess and Natalie's. Write instructions on cards to take from a pile at random. To make it more interesting, add the words 'clockwise' and 'anti-clockwise' to the instructions.

Imperial measures

Liam and his grandma decide to bake a cake together. Grandma's recipe gives measurements in imperial units but her new weighing scales are in metric units. She knows that 1 pound (lb) is 16 ounces (oz) and 1 ounce (oz) is about the same as 30 grams (g).

These are all the ingredients they need to weigh. Complete the table showing the metric measures they should use.

	Imperial	Metric
Butter	1 lb	
Self-raising flour	8 oz	
Caster sugar	6 oz	
Raisins	4 oz	
Cherries	2 oz	

They also need some liquid ingredients. Grandma knows that 1 pint is 568ml. They need half a pint of milk. How many ml is this? Explain how you know.

....

....

Liam estimates that a pint is just over half a litre. Using his estimation, can you compare each pair of measurements by adding one of these symbols: < > =

ⓐ 1 pint ◯ 1 litre   ⓑ 5 litres ◯ 5 pints

ⓒ 3 litres ◯ 6 pints   ⓓ 10 litres ◯ 20 pints

(e) Liam helps Grandma make a pie. They need to roll out some pastry. Grandma tells Liam he needs to roll out half a foot of pastry for the base and 4 inches for the lid, but his ruler only has metric measures marked. She tells him that 1 foot = 30cm and 1 inch = 2.5cm.

How many cm should he measure? ....

Grandma gives Liam some more measurements to practise converting. Can you help Liam by matching these imperial and metric measurements?

3 feet	10cm
4 inches	0.45m
$1\frac{1}{2}$ feet	90cm

Over dinner, Grandma checks what Liam has learnt by playing 'Would you rather...?' Assuming Liam likes each thing, what do you think he answered to each question?

(f) 1 pint of hot chocolate or 1 litre of hot chocolate? ....

(g) 3 inches of chocolate or 3cm of chocolate? ....

(h) 1 foot of pound coins in a line or 1m of pound coins in a line? ....

(i) 20 ounces of sweets or 20g of sweets? ....

(j) 1 pound of strawberries or 1 kilogram of strawberries? ....

Answers on page 64

PARENT TIP: Give children lots of opportunities in everyday life to use metric and imperial measurements. Encourage your child to do the weighing when you are baking and use recipes that have both units. Look at tape measures and use both sides to play games. For example, ask how many cm are in 6 inches, then turn the tape to see if they were right!

Perimeter and area

Sasha loves ice skating and has visited lots of different ice rinks. She likes to have lots of space to move around. Which of these is the biggest? Find their areas and write it on the dotted lines, then write numbers in the circle next to each one to show which is the biggest from 1 to 5.

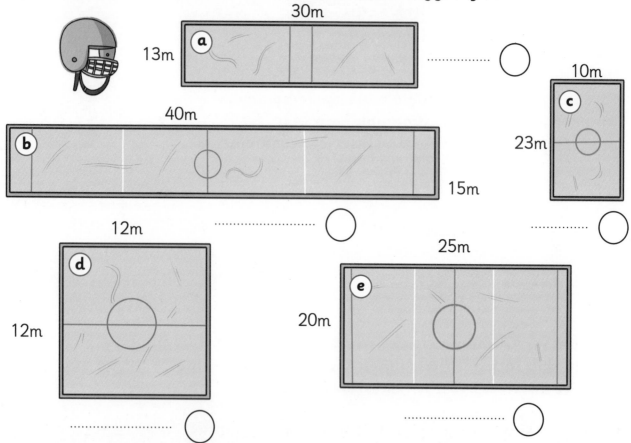

30m

a 13m .... ◯

40m

b 15m .... ◯

10m

c 23m .... ◯

12m

d 12m .... ◯

25m

e 20m .... ◯

In the winter, she often goes to outdoor ice rinks like this one.
Can you estimate its area by counting the squares on the square grid?
(Count any square greater than half as a whole and any less than half as 0). Write the area on the dotted line below.

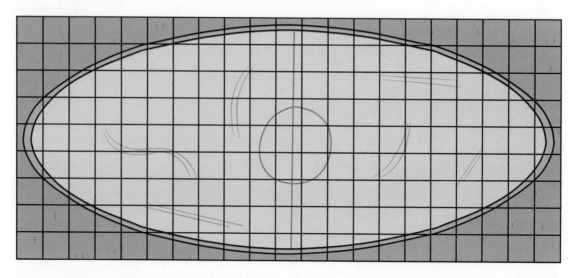

....

At Sasha's favourite ice rink, they are repainting the walls. The buildings are all different shapes. Can you work out the perimeter of each building so the decorators can work out how much paint they need? The manager has forgotten to measure some walls but can you work out the missing measures?

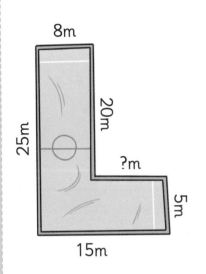

8m
25m
20m
?m
15m
5m

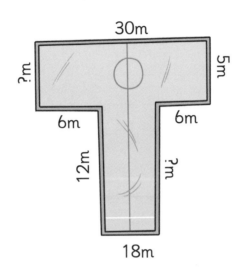

30m
?m
5m
6m
6m
12m
?m
18m

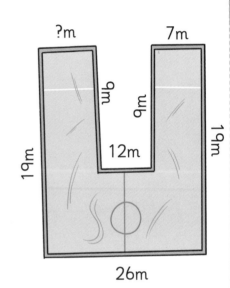

?m
7m
9m
9m
12m
19m
19m
26m

Perimeter: ....

Perimeter: ....

Perimeter: ....

For one more ice rink, the perimeter is 120m. Can you answer the calculations below?

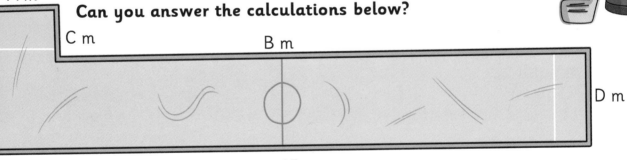

A m
C m
B m
15m
D m
45m

A + B = ...

C + D = ...

Answers on page 64

Answers on page 64

PARENT TIP: Help your children to measure the length and width of the rooms in your house. Which room has the biggest floor area? Which room has the longest perimeter?

61

Line graphs

Jay was given a drone for his birthday and went straight outside to test it out. The drone records its height above ground every minute, which you can see in this line graph.

Jay's Drone

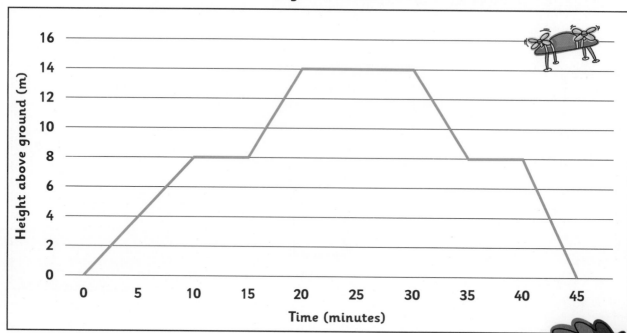

(a) How high was the drone after 5 minutes?

....

(b) How long does Jay keep his drone at 8m above the ground?

....

(c) How much does the drone's height increase by between 15 minutes and 20 minutes?

....

(d) How long does it take for the drone to reach its highest point?

....

(e) How long does it take for the drone to go from its highest point down to the ground?

....

Jay's friend, Martha, has come around with her drone and the two of them compete to see who can keep their drone in the air for the longest time.

Martha's Drone

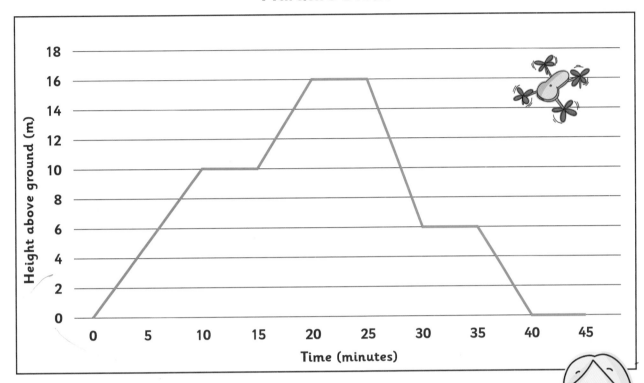

Whose drone goes higher than 10m above the ground first?

....

How much higher is Martha's drone after 20 minutes than Jay's?

....

For how much longer does Jay's drone stay at the highest point than Martha's?

....

Whose drone lands on the ground first? How much is the difference in minutes?

....

Answers on page 64

PARENT TIP: Encourage your child to draw their own graphs by collecting data from the things they do every day. This type of graph is suitable for measurements that change over time, such as the height of a plant growing in the garden or the distance travelled on a long journey.

Answers

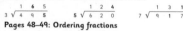

Page 34: Big numbers
1. two hundred and sixty thousand seven hundred and forty-five pounds.
2. two hundred and twenty-five thousand nine hundred and eighty-five pounds
3. two hundred and nine thousand four hundred and fifty-nine pounds
4. two hundred and twenty-nine thousand nine hundred and ninety-five pounds.
Correct order: £209 459 (house 3), £225 985 (house 2), £229 995 (house 4), £260 745 (house 1).
Reduced by: 1. £16 000 2. £8 000 3. £20 000 4. £2 000.

Page 35: Decimal numbers
House 2 has 5 tenths but the others have less than 5 tenths so are all smaller.

2.015 km   2.05 km   2.155 km   2.5 km

House 1 is closest to Jamie's friend's house.

Pages 36–37: Multiplying and dividing by 10, 100 and 1000
There were 23 000 fans altogether.   342 × 10 = 3420
7.5 × 1000 = 7500   100 × 24 = 2400   100 × 30 = 3000

	x1	x10	x100	x1000
Fizzy drinks	£1.99	£19.90	£199	£1990
Portion of chips	£2.30	£23	£230	£2300
Burgers	£3.50	£35	£350	£3500
Popcorn	£2.05	£20.50	£205	£2050
Chocolate bars	£0.95	£9.50	£95	£950

1. millilitres   2. tonnes   3. metres   4. grams

0.02kg   95g   130g   0.45kg   0.5kg

Pages 38–39: Rounding whole numbers

Team	Fans	Nearest 1000	Nearest 10 000	Nearest 100 000
1	162 739	163 000	160 000	200 000
2	250 182	250 000	250 000	300 000
3	306 873	307 000	310 000	300 000

a. Answers are any three numbers between 223 500–224 499 inclusive.
b. No, because any number above 177 500 rounds up to 178 000.
c. Team 6: 24 499, Team 7: 24 500. **d.** Lower tier. **e.** £89 **f.** Lucy rounded to the nearest £10 and Rory to the nearest £1. **g.** Lucy is correct: the 4 of the £24 rounds down to £20, not up to £30. **h.** Smallest: £22.50, largest: £23.49. **i.** Away kit OR home kit (both answers are correct).

Page 40: Adding and subtracting mentally
£224 + £228: near doubles.   £416 + £532 + £224: reordering.
£532 + £1425: partitioning.   £1425 + £199: rounding and adjusting.
a. 2345 − 1999 = 2345 − 2000 + 1 = 346. **b.** £1075.
c. 1465 + 335 (makes 1800) and 270 + 15 + 15 (makes 300), then 1800 + 300 (makes 2100).

Page 41: Adding and subtracting with written methods

January	February	March
239 962	161 528	97 037
− 182 045	− 94 387	− 87 238
57 917	67 141	9 799

Profits were most down in February. Tim rounded to the nearest ten thousand. (Last year: 240 000 + 160 000 + 100 000 = 500 000. This year: 180 000 + 90 000 + 90 000 = 360 000).

239 962	182 085
161 528	94 387
+ 97 037	+ 87 238
498 527	363 710

Pages 42–43: Multiples

Tom: 18 42 9 21   12 36 48 24   8 32 20 44 : Finlay

a. 12, 24, 36, 48. These are multiples of 12. **b.** 60, 72, 84.
c. Square numbers. **d.** Example answers: 4, 36, 49, 64, 81, 100. **e.** 3 × 3 × 3 = 27, 4 × 4 × 4 = 64, 5 × 5 × 5 = 125.
f. Tom: upper legs, Fran: lower legs, 7 shots. **g.** Fran: upper legs, Finley: hands, 12 shots. **h.** Finlay: arms, Tom: hands, 8 shots. **i.** No, it is because they are prime numbers. **j.** Any three answers from 7, 11, 13, 19, 23, 29.

Pages 44–45: Multiplying mentally
a. £3.40 **b.** £49 **c.** £17 **d.** 13 × 4 × 2 **e.** 23 × 10 − 23 **f.** 11 × 7 + 11 (she should add 7, not 11). **g.** £390 **h.** £405 **i.** £140 **j.** £175 **k.** £264. Children's tickets make the most money. **l.** Poppy doubled four times. She should have doubled three times. **m.** She should have added 9, not 13.
n. Multiplying any number by 0 = 0.

Page 46: Dividing mentally
a. 148 ÷ 2 ÷ 2 = £37 **b.** 230 ÷ 10 x 2 = £46 **c.** 630 ÷ 7 = £90

Page 47: Dividing with written methods
a. £55 **b.** £89.25 **c.** £56.50 **d.** £171.50

3) 4 9 5 = 1 6 5
5) 6 2 0 = 1 2 4
7) 9 1 7 = 1 3 1

Pages 48–49: Ordering fractions
Lucy $\frac{1}{3} = \frac{3}{9}$ **a.** > **b.** < **c.** > **d.** >
$\frac{3}{10} > \frac{1}{5}$ $\frac{3}{4} < \frac{8}{9}$ or $\frac{7}{8}$ $\frac{2}{3} > \frac{1}{5}$ or $\frac{2}{9}$ or $\frac{3}{7}$ $\frac{1}{4} > \frac{1}{5}$

*This denominator can be any digit greater than 4.

$2\frac{1}{3} = \frac{7}{3}$ $5\frac{1}{2} = \frac{11}{2}$ $1\frac{5}{8} = \frac{13}{8}$ $3\frac{3}{4} = \frac{15}{4}$
a. > **b.** < **c.** < **d.** >

$2\frac{1}{4} + \frac{7}{4} = \frac{9}{4} + \frac{7}{4} = \frac{16}{4} = \frac{4}{1}$ = 4 pizzas

$2\frac{1}{5} + \frac{12}{5} = \frac{11}{5} + \frac{12}{5} = \frac{23}{5} = 4\frac{3}{5}$ ice creams

Pages 50–51: Adding and subtracting fractions

	Sean	Robin	Total
Monday	$\frac{1}{5}$	$\frac{7}{10}$	$\frac{1}{5} + \frac{7}{10} = \frac{2}{10} + \frac{7}{10} = \frac{9}{10}$
Tuesday	$\frac{3}{4}$	$\frac{3}{12}$	$\frac{3}{4} + \frac{3}{12} = \frac{9}{12} + \frac{3}{12} = \frac{12}{12} = 1$
Wednesday	$\frac{1}{2}$	$\frac{2}{5}$	$\frac{1}{2} + \frac{2}{5} = \frac{5}{10} + \frac{4}{10} = \frac{9}{10}$
Thursday	$\frac{2}{3}$	$\frac{1}{5}$	$\frac{2}{3} + \frac{1}{5} = \frac{10}{15} + \frac{3}{15} = \frac{13}{15}$
Friday	$\frac{1}{6}$	$\frac{3}{8}$	$\frac{1}{6} + \frac{3}{8} = \frac{4}{24} + \frac{9}{24} = \frac{13}{24}$

	Amount at start of day	Amount at end of day	Total
Monday	$\frac{3}{4}$	$\frac{5}{8}$	$\frac{3}{4} - \frac{5}{8} = \frac{6}{8} - \frac{5}{8} = \frac{1}{8}$
Tuesday	$1\frac{1}{5}$	$\frac{7}{10}$	$\frac{6}{5} - \frac{7}{10} = \frac{12}{10} - \frac{7}{10} = \frac{5}{10} = \frac{1}{2}$
Wednesday	$1\frac{1}{3}$	$\frac{5}{12}$	$\frac{4}{3} - \frac{5}{12} = \frac{16}{12} - \frac{5}{12} = \frac{11}{12}$
Thursday	$1\frac{1}{6}$	$\frac{3}{4}$	$\frac{7}{6} - \frac{3}{4} = \frac{28}{24} - \frac{18}{24} = \frac{10}{24} = \frac{5}{12}$
Friday	$1\frac{2}{3}$	$\frac{3}{5}$	$\frac{5}{3} - \frac{3}{5} = \frac{25}{15} - \frac{9}{15} = \frac{16}{15}$

a. $\frac{2}{3} \times 3 = \frac{6}{3} = 2$ **b.** $\frac{3}{4} \times 5 = \frac{15}{4} = 3\frac{3}{4}$ **c.** $\frac{2}{5} \times 4 = \frac{8}{5} = 1\frac{3}{5}$ **d.** $\frac{2}{4} \times 6 = \frac{12}{4} = \frac{6}{2} = 3$

Pages 52–53: Percentages
$\frac{1}{2}$=50%=0.5 $\frac{3}{4}$=75%=0.75 $\frac{2}{5}$=40%=0.4 $\frac{4}{5}$=80%=0.8 $\frac{1}{10}$=10%=0.1
$\frac{1}{25}$, 0.25, 30%, 0.6, $\frac{8}{10}$

a. 30% **b.** $\frac{1}{5}$ **c.** 0.4 **d.** Sadie by 5% or $\frac{1}{20}$ or 0.05 **e.** $\frac{3}{20}$ **f.** 50%

Pages 54–55: Shapes

Regular polygons	Irregular polygons

(In a regular shape, all sides will be the same length and all of the angles will be the same. Irregular shapes have lengths and angles of different measurements.)
a. No, it needs 3 equal sides. **b.** No, it also needs equal sides. **c.** All sides should be equal. All angles should be equal.

Hexagonal prism: 6 rectangular faces, 2 hexagonal faces, 12 vertices, 18 edges
Square-based pyramid: 1 square face, 4 triangular faces, 5 vertices, 8 edges
Triangular prism: 3 rectangular faces, 2 triangular faces, 6 vertices, 9 edges
Cylinder: 2 circular faces, 1 curved face, 0 vertices, 2 edges
Cuboid: 6 rectangular faces, 3 pairs of equal faces, 8 vertices, 12 edges
Triangular-based pyramid: 4 triangular faces, 4 vertices, 6 edges

Pages 56–57: Angles

a. 55⁰ b. 80⁰ c. 80⁰

Natalie faces the start again first.

d. 160⁰   e. 90⁰   f. 188⁰   g. 175⁰   h. 112⁰

Pages 58–59: Imperial measures
Butter - 1 pound - 480g
Self raising flour - 8oz - 240g
Caster sugar - 6oz - 180g
Raisins - 4oz - 120g
Cherries - 2oz - 60g

Half a pint of milk is 284ml (because it is half of 568ml)
a. < **b.** > **c.** < **d.** < **e.** base: 15cm / lid: 10cm
3 feet and 90cm / 4 inches and 10cm / $1\frac{1}{2}$ feet and 0.45m
f. 1 litre **g.** 3 inches **h.** 1 metre **i.** 20 ounces **j.** 1kg

Pages 60–61: Perimeter and area
a. 390m² (3)   b. 600m² (5)   c. 230m² (2)   d. 144m² (1)   e. 500m² (4)

Area of oval: approximately 126m² (answer may vary)

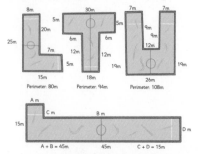

Perimeter: 80m   Perimeter: 94m   Perimeter: 108m

A + B = 45m   45m   C + D = 15m

Pages 62–63: Line graphs
a. 4 metres **b.** 5 minutes between 5–10 minutes and 5 minutes between 35–40 minutes, so 10 minutes in total. **c.** 6 metres **d.** 20 minutes **e.** 15 minutes **f.** Martha's **g.** 2 metres **h.** 5 minutes **i.** Martha's. The difference is 5 minutes.

10-11 years

Key Stage 2

Leap Ahead
BUMPER
Workbook

ENGLISH

Home learning made FUN!

Adjectives or adverbs?

Look at the sentences below. They are all scrambled! Can you re-arrange the words so that the sentences make sense? After that, sort the words into the boxes by type.

enthusiastically the spaniel at postman. The leapt

....

....

Some children playing the in park. joyfully were

....

....

from tiny wandered The mother. had lamb its

....

....

Determiners	Adjectives	Adverbs

Nouns	Verbs	Prepositions

Answers on page 96

Devise your device!

Find the picture sticker that matches each sentence then circle the correct homophone for each one. The homophone is either a noun or a verb.

place sticker here	I am going to basketball practise/practice.
place sticker here	I am going to practice/practise my basketball skills.
place sticker here	Matt enjoys creating new worlds on his device/devise.
place sticker here	Matt enjoys trying to device/devise new worlds.

Sort the homophones above into nouns and verbs in the table then add some more of your own homophones to the table.

Nouns	Verbs

Answers on page 96

Clauses and phrases

A noun phrase tells you more about a noun.

the large, shiny balloon in the sky

In this noun phrase, you can tell the balloon is large and shiny and it is in the sky.

Underline the noun phrase in this sentence:

The large yellow umbrella above his head kept him from getting wet.

Adverbial phrases tell you how, when and where the action is happening.

Underline two adverbial phrases in this sentence:

The boy went fishing at sunset on the choppy waves.

Extra clauses can also add detail. Subordinate clauses begin with a subordinating conjunction, such as *when, because, while, after, as, if, before*.

The sand was a yellow, gold colour on the beach <u>when the sun started to set.</u>

Underline the subordinate clauses in the sentences below and draw rings around the conjunctions.

The puppy started to bark because it saw the postman arrive.

After they had unpacked, the family explored the holiday cottage.

They visited the swimming pool while it was raining.

Answers on page 96

PARENT TIP: A phrase is a group of words that doesn't have a verb. A main clause has a noun and a verb. Look at a book or magazine article with your child and try to find examples of both phrases and main clauses.

Lists

We can write lists in two different ways using either bullet points or semi-colons. For a trip to the Moon, we could write:

These are the items required for a trip to the Moon:
- a white space helmet
- astronaut suit
- freeze-dried food
- a moon buggy

OR

These are the items required for a trip to the Moon: a white space helmet; astronaut suit; freeze-dried food and a moon buggy.

Imagine you're going on a trip to Antarctica. Some of the items in the suitcase below are appropriate for your trip but others might not be very useful. Cross out the items you won't need, then use the stickers on the sticker sheet to add more items that you will need. Write two lists of the items — one using bullet-points and one using semi-colons.

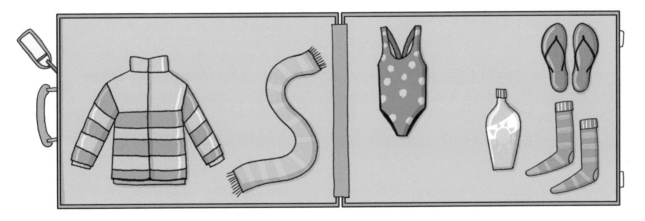

These are the items required for my trip to Antarctica:

....

....

....

....

....

....

These are the items required for my trip to Antarctica:

....

....

....

....

....

....

Antonyms and synonyms

Antonyms are words that have opposite meanings. Synonyms are words that have the same meaning.

Find the synonyms for *happy* from the selection below. Put a tick sticker from the sticker sheet next to each one.

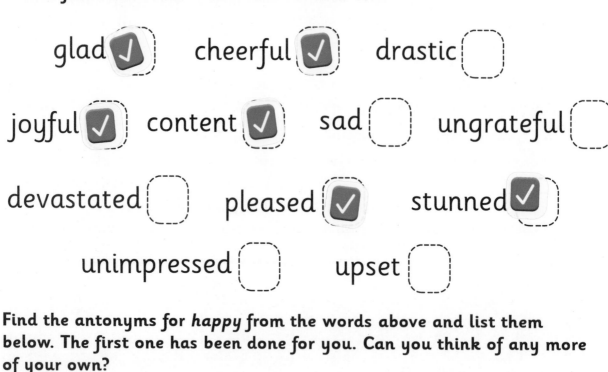

glad ✓   cheerful ✓   drastic ☐

joyful ✓   content ✓   sad ☐   ungrateful ☐

devastated ☐   pleased ✓   stunned ✓

unimpressed ☐   upset ☐

Find the antonyms for *happy* from the words above and list them below. The first one has been done for you. Can you think of any more of your own?

Upset, devastated   sad unimpressed

Circle the synonym that matches the word on the left.

1. cold   warm chilly toasty boiling
2. drink   consume scoff laugh lag

Circle the antonym for each of the words on the left.

3. rush   dawdle walk hurry dash
4. frightened scared alarmed rushed calm

Answers on page 96

Subject, verb, object

In English grammar, sentences are built following the same order. Every sentence has a subject and a verb in that order. Many also have an object. Try to remember this as *SV* and *SVO*.

The subject in a sentence performs the action.
The verb is the action.
The object has the action done to it.

Granny	was eating	a jam sandwich.
subject	**verb**	**object**

If we change the order, it doesn't work. Look at these!

Granny a jam sandwich was eating. *SOV (subject object verb)*

Was eating Granny a jam sandwich. *VSO (verb subject object)*

Rewrite the following sentences in the correct *SVO* order then label the subject, object and verb using the symbols *S V* and *O*.

Johnny a new jumper. was wearing

Johnny was wearing a new Jumper

a ball. was juggling A clown

A clown was juggling a ball

is drinking Jane a glass of orange juice.

Jane is drinking a glass of orange juice

Answers on page 96

PARENT TIP: If your child is finding this exercise challenging, remind them that some verbs are verb chains where you have more than one verb describing the action (e.g. *could have done* or *have been running*).

Lights, camera, action!

Write a sentence to describe what is happening in each picture.
Remember to use *SVO*. Circle the subject in each of your sentences.

Writing like a reporter

When you write like a reporter, you often change your writing from active voice to passive voice. In active voice, the subject does the action (e.g. *The shark chased the swimmer.*).
In passive voice, the subject is having the action done to it (e.g. *The swimmer was being chased by the shark.*).

To change from active to passive, the object in the active sentence becomes the subject in a passive sentence:

The shark chased <u>the swimmer</u>.
<u>The swimmer</u> was being chased by the shark.

Change these sentences from active to passive:

Active	Passive
The boy broke the phone.	The phone was broken by the boy.
We left rubbish in the field.	Rubbish was left ....
A robot attacked the buildings.	The buildings ....
The superhero saved the child.	....

Reporter's notebook

You need to be careful not to mention who is to blame when you are writing newspaper reports unless you are absolutely sure you know who did it! Passive voice is useful for this because you can leave out who did it. For example: *The window was smashed.*

Have a go! Write a sentence of your own but leave out who did it.

....

....

....

....

Answers on page 96

Find the features

Look at the different types of text across these two pages. Find a sticker to name each text type, then choose some layout features from the mirror on page 75 and list them underneath. You can use each feature for more than one text type.

1

Rice Puff Cakes

You will need:
- 100g chocolate
- 75g rice puffs
- 12 cake cases

Method:
1. Melt the chocolate in a bowl over a pan of hot water. Get an adult to help you.
2. Stir the rice puffs into the melted chocolate, a few at a time. Ensure they are fully coated in chocolate.
3. Spoon enough mixture into each cake case.
4. Chill in the fridge until hard.
5. Enjoy!

....

....

place sticker here

2

SUPERHERO SAVES BABY

Yesterday in Big City, a young child was saved by a superhero who was flying past on the way back to his lair.

He was able to catch the child who was falling from a 27th floor window.

....

....

place sticker here

Answers on page 96

(3)

Gorillas

These shy and gentle creatures are one of the five types of ape. Gorillas are closely related in DNA to humans. They live in rainforests in family groups.

....

....

place sticker
here

Layout features:

(4)

28th June

90 Forest Lane
Greenton Woods

Dear Grandad,

Thank you very much for the money you sent me for my birthday. I had a wonderful day and I enjoyed playing with my friends.

I shall look forward to spending the money you sent me on a new game.

Best wishes,
Jessie

title
columns
factual
address
heading
bullet points
informal
numbers
formal

....

place sticker here

....

Answers on page 96

Ceilings to receipts

Do you know this rule: "i before e, except after c, when rhyming with ee"? This means the *ee* sound in *chief* is spelt *ie*, but the same sound in *receive* is spelt *ei*.

ie   cei

Some words don't obey the rule! Look out for: *protein*, *caffeine* and *seize*!

Have a go at spelling the words below. They are spelt with *ei* or *ie*.

dec_ei_ve   rec_ei_ve   perc_ei_ve   c_ei_ling

rec_ei_pt   v_ei_n   w_ei_gh   rel_ief_

Can you find those same words in this word search? Look horizontally, vertically and diagonally. Tick each one once you've found it.

a	c	i	n	g	w	d	n	e	i	v	e
d	h	f	o	z	p	e	f	z	m	p	d
l	n	l	k	r	e	c	e	i	v	e	j
m	h	o	r	b	j	e	h	b	e	r	c
s	q	c	e	i	l	i	n	g	i	c	e
h	w	x	c	r	w	v	a	o	v	e	i
j	m	c	e	j	e	e	q	p	e	i	p
k	v	e	i	n	a	l	i	s	k	v	t
l	o	s	p	f	x	u	i	g	c	e	a
y	j	n	t	d	h	j	l	e	h	b	f
b	q	u	o	e	i	v	e	h	f	d	h

Answers on page 96

Colons

You have learned how to use a colon in a list earlier in this book. Colons also help to explain, reveal and emphasise. Colons are the bling of writing – you mustn't use them too often as they are special!

<u>Rules</u>
The first clause has to stand alone. You should be able to add a full stop at the end of the first clause. You don't need a capital letter after the colon. A word, phrase or clause can follow a colon.

He had been excited all weekend: it was his birthday sleepover!

This painting was by her favourite artist: Van Gogh.

Look at the pictures below. Write a sentence about each picture using a colon to reveal, explain or emphasise. The first one is done for you.

He gently peeled back the shiny, red paper. He pulled the paper at one corner and then he saw it: the game he had always wanted.

....
....
....
....

....
....
....

Referring to the referee

Read the text below. Look out for words with *fer* in the middle of them and underline them.

"Goal!" she shouted. The referee blew his whistle, but the red team asked for a referral. After the decision had been referred, the goal was allowed and play continued. The centre for the blue team preferred sprinting up the left of the pitch. He reached the box and transferred the ball in. Boom! Another goal was scored by the red team. The goalkeeper should have stopped that one but he was conferring with the coach at the time!

The blue team got the ball and set off down the pitch, making a transference from left to right. Suddenly, a red player fell. She got up, muttering that she preferred wearing her other boots as they helped her run more steadily.

The whistle blew for the end of the match. Player of the match was chosen by the manager who had a preference for players who worked hard and played fair. She was referring to several players in the game but picked one of the blues and made reference to his ability to cross the ball and pass well. She hoped he wouldn't be transferring to another team!

Sometimes you have to double the last *r* when *fer* is in a word. It all depends where the stress is on the word.

Referral: you emphasise *fer* in this word so you do have to double the last *r* before adding *al*.

Referee: you emphasise *ref* in this word so you don't need to double the last *r* before adding *ee*.

Sort the *fer* words from the text into this table, according to the rules.

Emphasise *fer* in the word so you double the last *r*	Don't emphasise *fer* in the word so you don't double the last *r*
referral	referee

Answers on page 96

For or against

Year 6 pupils should be allowed to eat sugary snacks at break time.

Read the different viewpoints below and place a "for" or "against" sticker next to each statement, to show whether they are in favour of the argument or not.

place sticker here | Children enjoy eating chocolates and biscuits.

place sticker here | Too many sugary snacks are bad for your teeth.

place sticker here | You should eat fruit at break to increase your 5-a-day.

place sticker here | Some sugary snacks give you instant energy.

place sticker here | It takes too much time to prepare fruit and vegetables.

place sticker here | Eating a variety of fruit and vegetables increases your vitamins.

Write a paragraph below to explain each point of view.
Practise linking statements together using conjunctions and adverbs.

Adverbs: *whereas, in contrast, on the other hand, however*
Conjunctions: *while, even though, although, despite*

Should Year 6 pupils be allowed to eat sugary snacks at break time?

....
....
....
....
....
....
....
....

Answers on page 96

Points of view

Should mobile phones be allowed in Year 6 classrooms? Consider the viewpoints of pupils, teachers, parents and a mobile phone company. List the points of view for each of the groups. Use bullet points to note your ideas.

Child's point of view	Teacher's point of view

Parent's point of view	Mobile phone company's point of view

Discussion

Should mobile phones be allowed in Year 6 classrooms? Write up the points of view into a discussion text. Consider each point of view, both for and against.

In your writing, use paragraphs to organise the points of view, and adverbs and conjunctions to link your ideas.

Ending with *ible* or *able*?

Draw lines from the root words on the left to the suffix *ible* or *able* on the right to make words.

vis

depend

expend

horr

enjoy

reason

terr

incred

able

ible

How many *ible* and *able* words can you use? Write two sentences below using as many *ible* and *able* words as you can.

....

....

....

....

....

Answers on page 96

PARENT TIP: Usually, *able* is used when you can hear the full root word (e.g. *comfort/comfortable*) and *ible* is used when you can't hear the full root word (e.g. *audio/audible*).

Informal conversation

When we chat to or message our friends, we speak and write informally. We use contractions (*I'm, I've, we'll*) and question tags (*That film was great, wasn't it?*). Below, practise writing an informal conversation with a friend. Use contractions and question tags. Think about how you would speak to your friend and what you might ask them.

Received 12:30

Sent 12:33

Received 13:25

Sent 13:57

Received 14:02

If I were you...

Look at the pictures on the right and write speech for each scene. Use the subjunctive forms of verbs in the red boxes.

If I were you, I would buy that green jumper.

No, thanks. I prefer blue.

If I were you, ...

....

....

I demand that you ....

....

....

May I request that ....

....

I hope that you will ....

....

PARENT TIP: The subjunctive is used to express wishes, demands or requests which are often not factual or doubtful. It is often written in the form of a subordinate clause using *that* or *if*.

I'm on holiday

Write a postcard to describe a holiday you've been on. Use the checklist below to ensure you've included everything, ticking off each point once you've done it.

Postcard-writing checklist:

☐ **Noun phrases to describe the location**

☐ **Informal writing style**

☐ **Question tags**

☐ **Subjunctive (e.g. *wish you were here*)**

Puzzling punctuation

Complete the multiple choice quiz by choosing the correct punctuation to match the statement. Write your answers in the spaces provided.

1. Two sets of inverted commas that are used at the start and the end of someone speaking:
   - a) commas
   - b) speech marks
   - c) brackets
   - d) full stops

2. Two types of punctuation that demarcate a relative clause (choose two):
   - a) full stops
   - b) brackets
   - c) exclamation marks
   - d) commas

3. Punctuation after a main clause that introduces a list:
   - a) semi-colon
   - b) full stop
   - c) colon
   - d) comma

4. Punctuation used after a subordinate clause at the start of a sentence:
   - a) comma
   - b) full stop
   - c) semi-colon
   - d) brackets

5. Three types of punctuation that can be used to indicate parenthesis:
   - a) commas, full stops and colons
   - b) commas, brackets and dashes
   - c) dashes, full stops and semi-colons
   - d) speech marks, commas and brackets

My answers:
1. ____   2. ____   3. ____   4. ____   5. ____

Answers on page 96

Semi-colons

Semi-colons link two clauses and either add further information or contrast information. The two clauses must be closely linked. If you can use *and* or *but* to link the sentence, then you could try using a semi-colon instead. For example:

It was raining heavily but the match was still on.

It was raining heavily; the match was still on.

Add a semi-colon sticker from the sticker sheet at the end of the first main clause, then write your own second clause which is linked.

(a) The car had stopped in the middle of the road ....

....

(b) The child fell from the kitchen table ....

....

(c) Suddenly, the walls crashed all around her ....

....

(d) They trudged and trudged up the hill ....

....

(e) I am writing to complain ....

....

(f) You should definitely buy this game ....

....

....

Nutritious and delicious

You need to know whether to choose *c* or *t* when spelling words ending with *tious* or *cious*. The suffixes *cious* and *tious* mean "full of". For example, *gracious* means "full of grace".

When the root word ends in *ce*, the suffix is usually *cious* (e.g. *space* to *spacious*). If the root word ends in *tion*, it becomes *tious* (e.g. *nutrition* to *nutritious*).

Find the *ce*, *cious* and *tious* words in the word search below.

v	i	c	e	u	b	l	a	i	o	u	s	v	o	y
i	r	p	k	n	q	x	v	n	f	h	l	x	b	a
c	g	r	a	c	e	v	y	p	x	j	k	u	w	v
i	j	e	n	o	u	w	x	u	s	i	i	o	u	s
o	c	c	m	n	j	m	v	y	u	f	o	b	e	i
u	i	i	l	s	p	a	c	e	s	n	y	u	k	n
s	j	o	p	c	h	l	l	f	p	u	h	c	s	f
b	u	u	k	i	o	i	x	k	i	o	t	a	h	e
g	s	s	i	o	v	c	w	n	c	d	y	u	m	c
q	p	l	j	u	y	e	u	x	i	v	w	t	r	t
k	o	r	q	s	p	a	c	i	o	u	s	i	u	i
a	m	b	i	t	i	o	u	s	u	j	l	o	f	o
g	r	a	c	i	o	u	s	f	s	i	k	u	b	u
n	u	t	r	i	t	i	o	u	s	d	g	s	d	s

vice	space	ambitious
vicious	spacious	nutritious
unconscious	malice	cautious
grace	precious	infectious
gracious	suspicious	anxious

Answers on page 96

Dashes and hyphens

Do you know the difference between these punctuations marks? Dashes are longer and have a space either side of them. They are used to join clauses and phrases together. A pair of dashes either side of a phrase is used to add information in the middle of a sentence. A single dash is used if information is added at the end. Choose stickers from the sheet to make the sentences make sense.

1. The monster [place sticker here] had captured the ice maiden.

2. We went shopping and I bought a new top [place sticker here]

3. Making colourful slime [place sticker here] is the latest craze.

4. I can do 19 keep-ups with my football [place sticker here]

Hyphens are shorter and have no spaces either side. They join words together, for example to make compound adjectives. Write the words from the box into the correct spaces below.

> ear-piercing   well-known   friendly-looking
> pitch-black   meat-eating

1. Ruby stroked the .... dog.

2. Everyone queued up to meet the .... internet star.

3. T-rex was a .... dinosaur.

4. At Year 6 camp, we crept around to find the entrance to our tent in the .... night.

5. An .... scream was heard.

Answers on page 96

May I suggest...

We often use formal sentences when writing, but informal ones when speaking. Look for the matching formal/informal pairs and draw lines between them. One has been done for you.

May I please have your address?

I request the presence of your company at our annual meeting.

One of my main passions is research into felines.

I suggest that you consider this proposal.

Yours Sincerely, Thomas Large

I strongly recommend that you visit this castle.

I love cats!

Can I have your address?

Love from Tom x

Would you like to visit the castle?

I've got a great idea.

I would like to ask you to join us.

Read each sentence below then re-write it in a more formal way.

The snow is very cold. You'll need a scarf and gloves.

....

I can't wait to see you next weekend!

....

The theme park is going to be great!

....

Do you want to read this book? I liked it a lot.

....

90

Answers on page 96

Edit and evaluate

Read this paragraph. Look for the weak word choices (in bold) and change them to some better word choices of your own.

In a city in Rome called Pompeii, a volcano **happened**. The blast was so sudden that people didn't have a chance to escape. Some people **went** to the harbour and got away on a boat. Boiling lava and hot ash **popped** from the top of the volcano and covered the whole city. It was **sad**.

Proofread this paragraph and identify words spelt incorrectly. Change the spellings.

Valcanos cause many problems in the enviroment. Firstly, the tempriture and preshure of the volcano builds up and causes explocians. The naturel disastor has great strenth and the lava from volcanos can distroy trees or buildings in its parth.

Proofread this final paragraph for punctuation errors. Think about all the different types of punctuation covered in this book. Cross out incorrect punctuation and add in the correct punctuation.

Dear Diary,

What a horrendous day weve had? I cant believe what has happened in our city a volcano has erupted from Mount Vesuvious? We was so lucky because we live near the coast. As soon as we saw, the ash and smoke my dad told us to get in his fishing boat. We looked back from the harbour and saw the lava pour down the mountainside We had a really lucky escape. Ill never forget my life in Pompeii.

Answers on page 96

Possibility

Find the modal verb and adverb stickers on the sticker sheet.
Order them on the line below from possible to definite.

possible

|

definite

Choose a modal verb and an adverb to complete these sentences.

It .... snow tomorrow.

School .... be closed for a year.

The world .... spin on its axis
for 24 hours.

Orangutans .... walk on all fours.

We .... include everyone in our game.

Big spelling test

Can you spell all of these words? You have practised all the rules for them in this book. Ask an adult to test you or write out your spellings then check them yourself.

important

transferred

transparency

incredible

horribly

dependable

thief

practice

advise

licence

anxious

environment

deceive

spacious

cautious

referee

reasonable

piece

reference

Writing to complain

Choose a topic to complain about from the list below, then plan a letter of complaint. Write your letter on the following page. Use the checklist to help you, ticking off each point once you've included it.

Checklist:

- [ ] I've included a wide range of punctuation including semi-colons.
- [ ] I've used the subjunctive form.
- [ ] I've written in passive voice.
- [ ] I've used formal vocabulary and a formal tone.

Complaint topics to choose from:

- **All break times are going to be cancelled in your school, except 15 minutes to eat lunch.**
- **All mobile phones and gaming devices are going to be banned for under 13s.**
- **Homework is increasing to 3 hours every weekend.**

Homework

Answers

Page 66: Adjectives or adverbs?

The spaniel leapt enthusiastically at the postman.
Some children were playing joyfully in the park.
The tiny lamb had wandered from its mother.
Determiners: The, the, Some, the, The, its **Adjectives:** tiny
Nouns: spaniel, postman, children, park, lamb, mother
Verbs: leapt, were playing, had wandered
Adverbs: enthusiastically, joyfully **Prepositions:** at, in, from

Page 67: Devise your device!

I am going to basketball (practice) I am going to (practise) my
basketball skills. Matt enjoys creating new worlds on his (device).
Matt enjoys trying to (devise) new worlds.
Nouns: practice, device / Verbs: practise, devise

Page 68: Clauses and phrases

Noun phrase: The <u>large yellow umbrella above his head</u> kept
him from getting wet.
Adverbial phrases: The boy went fishing <u>at sunset</u> <u>on the</u>
<u>choppy waves</u>.
Subordinate clauses: The puppy started to bark (because)
<u>it saw the postman arrive.</u> / (After) <u>they had unpacked</u>, the
family explored the holiday cottage. / They visited the
swimming pool (while) <u>it was raining.</u>

Page 70: Antonyms and synonyms

Happy = glad / cheerful / content / joyful / pleased
Antonyms for happy = sad / devastated / upset / unimpressed
1. cold/chilly **2.** drink/consume **3.** rush/dawdle **4.** frightened/calm

Page 71: Subject, verb, object

(S) Johnny (V) was wearing (O) a new jumper.
(S) A clown (V) was juggling (O) a ball.
(S) Jane (V) is drinking (O) a glass of orange juice.

Page 73: Writing like a reporter

Rubbish was left in the field by us.
The buildings were attacked by a robot.
The child was saved by a superhero.

Pages 74–75: Find the features

1 = instructions. Features include: title, bullet points, numbers.
2 = newspaper report. Features include: columns, factual,
heading, formal.
3 = information report. Features include: title, factual.
4 = letter. Features include: address, informal.

Page 76: Ceilings to receipts

deceive, receive, perceive, ceiling, receipt, vein, weigh, relief

a	c	i	n	g	w	d	n	e	i	v	e
d	h	f	o	z	p	e	f	z	m	p	d
l	n	l	k	r	e	c	e	i	v	e	j
m	h	o	r	b	j	e	h	b	e	r	c
s	q	c	e	i	l	i	n	g	i	c	e
h	w	x	c	r	w	v	a	o	v	e	i
j	m	c	e	j	e	e	q	p	e	i	p
k	v	e	i	n	a	l	i	s	k	v	t
l	o	s	p	f	x	u	i	g	c	e	a
y	j	n	t	d	h	j	l	e	h	b	f
b	q	u	o	e	i	v	e	h	f	d	h

Page 78: Referring to the referee

Emphasise *fer* in the word: referral, referred, preferred,
transferred, conferring, preferred, referring, transferring
Don't emphasise *fer* in the word: referee, transference,
preference, reference

Page 79: For or against

For: Children enjoy eating chocolates and biscuits.
Against: Too many sugary snacks are bad for your teeth.
Against: You should eat fruit at break to increase your 5-a-day.
For: Some sugary snacks give you instant energy.
For: It takes too much time to prepare fruit and vegetables.
Against: Eating a variety of fruit and vegetables increases
your vitamins.

Page 82: Ending with *ible* or *able*?

visible/dependable/expendable/horrible/enjoyable/reasonable/terrible/incredible

Page 86: Puzzling punctuation

1. b **2.** b and d **3.** c **4.** a **5.** b

Page 88: Nutritious and delicious

v	i	c	e	u	b	l	a	i	o	u	s	v	o	y
i	r	p	k	n	q	x	n	f	h	l	x	b	a	
c	g	r	a	c	e	v	y	p	x	j	k	u	w	w
i	j	e	n	o	u	w	x	u	s	i	i	o	u	s
o	c	c	m	n	j	m	v	y	u	f	o	b	e	i
u	i	i	l	s	p	a	c	e	s	n	y	u	k	n
s	j	o	p	c	h	l	l	f	p	u	h	c	s	f
b	u	u	k	i	o	i	x	k	i	o	t	a	h	e
g	s	s	i	o	v	c	w	n	c	d	y	u	m	c
q	p	l	j	u	y	e	u	x	i	v	w	t	r	t
k	o	r	q	s	p	a	c	i	o	u	s	i	u	i
a	m	b	i	t	i	o	u	s	u	j	l	o	f	o
g	r	a	c	i	o	u	s	f	s	i	k	u	b	u
n	u	t	r	i	t	i	o	u	s	d	g	s	d	s

Page 89: Dashes and hyphens

1. – the one with the green eyes –   **2.** – I love it!
3. – which is very sticky and messy –   **4.** – can you?
1. friendly-looking   **2.** well-known   **3.** meat-eating
4. pitch-black   **5.** ear-piercing

Page 90: May I suggest...

May I please have your address? = Can I have your address?
I request the presence of your company at our annual meeting.
= I would like to ask you to join us.
One of my main passions is research into felines. = I love cats!
I suggest that you consider this proposal. = I've got a great idea.
Yours sincerely, Thomas Large = Love from Tom x
I strongly recommend that you visit this castle. = Would you like
to visit the castle?

Page 91: Edit and evaluate

Volcanoes cause many problems in the **environment**. Firstly,
the **temperature** and **pressure** of the volcano builds up and
causes **explosions**. The **natural disaster** has great **strength** and
the lava from **volcanoes** can **destroy** trees or buildings in its **path**.

Dear Diary,
What a horrendous day **we've** had! I **can't** believe what has
happened in our city: a volcano has erupted from Mount Vesuvious.
We **were** so lucky because we live near the coast. As soon as we
saw the ash and smoke, my dad told us to get in his fishing boat.
We looked back from the harbour and saw the lava pour down
the mountainside. We had a really lucky escape. **I'll** never forget
my life in Pompeii.

Leap Ahead
BUMPER
Workbook

MATHS

Home learning made FUN!

Big numbers

Robbie wants to be a professional footballer and he has been researching how much his favourite players earn.

Randles
£14 568 400

Finch
£8 235 938

Kinsman
£8 098 324

Hagarth
£15 408 276

Use the stickers on your sticker sheet to place the footballers' names in order of their wages from lowest to highest.

Lowest ———————————————————→ Highest

When their new contracts are released, their wages change according to how well they have played. Complete the table with their new wages.

player name	wage change	new wages
Randles	£600 000 decrease	
Finch	£70 000 increase	
Kinsman	£450 000 increase	
Hagarth	£9000 decrease	

Below are the wages of two more footballers. Can you insert the missing digit in each wage to show who earns the most? Choose two digits from your sticker sheet. There are several correct answers.

£2 32 ◯ 450 < £2 3 ◯ 3 640

Answers on page 128

Decimal numbers

Robbie and his friends play for a local football team. Their coach gives them fitness trackers to see how far they run during training. The trackers are set to kilometres.

Robbie's tracker shows 8.164 and James' shows 8.4. Robbie tells James, "I've run farthest because my distance has more digits."
Is Robbie correct? What should James say?

....

....

William has accidentally set his to metres (14 003m) so he divides it by 1000 to convert it to kilometres. He says he has run 14.3km. Is he right?

....

At the next training session, they all set their trackers to metres.
Can you divide their distances by 1000 to convert them to kilometres?

Robbie	Jenny	William	Poppy	Connor
12 042m	9802m	10 460m	15 800m	8045m

....

Robbie practises converting more distances but gets muddy fingerprints over the sums. Find the missing numbers on the sticker sheet.

$$1\ 3\ .\ 4\ k\ m\ \times\ \_\_\ =\ 1\ 3\ 4\ 0\ 0\ m$$

$$\_\_\ c\ m\ \div\ 1\ 0\ 0\ =\ 3\ 4\ m$$

Answers on page 128

PARENT TIP: Make flashcards with ×10, ×100, ×1000, ÷10, ÷100, ÷1000 and a mixture of whole numbers and decimal numbers, and divide into two piles. Take turns to pick up a flashcard from each pile and carry out the calculation, e.g. [3.41] [× 1000] = 3410. Whoever has the biggest answer wins the round.

Rounding numbers

Kyle's dad is looking to spend about £13 000 on a new car. Which of the cars at the dealership would round to £13 000 to the nearest thousand?

....

He agrees to buy the red car if the salesman will round it down to the nearest thousand. How much will he pay?

....

The salesman wants to round it down to the nearest hundred. What do you notice about the new price?

....

The salesman has got the new prices for some of the cars in a muddle. His manager gives him a clue about each price:

"The price on the red car rounds to £14 800 when rounded to the nearest hundred."

"The pink car's price rounds to the same number when rounded to the nearest ten or nearest hundred."

"The gold car's price rounds down to the nearest ten, hundred and thousand."

"The green car's price rounds to £20 000 to the nearest ten thousand."

Stick the correct price from the sticker sheet on the windscreen of each car.

Answers on page 128

Negative numbers

Sapna has been learning about the temperatures in different cities around the world. Can you help her to find the difference in temperatures between each pair of cities?

City	Temperature
Toronto	-7°C
London	13°C
Moscow	-18°C
Rio	28°C

Toronto and **London**   The difference is: _20°C_

Toronto and **Moscow**   The difference is: _11°C_

London and **Moscow**   The difference is: _31°C_

Moscow and **Rio**   The difference is: _46°C_

Toronto and **Rio**   The difference is: _35°C_

Sapna notices that the temperature in Warsaw drops by 10 degrees every month: 29°C, 19°C, 9°C...

She continues the sequence to estimate what the temperature will be in two more months if the pattern continues.

29°C, 19°C, 9°C, -9°C, -19°C

Can you explain and correct Sapna's mistake?

_29°C, 19°C 9°C -1°C -11°C_

Answers on page 128

PARENT TIP: Draw a number line from -20 to 20 with 0 at the halfway point. Place a counter at 0 and take turns to throw a dice. Player 1 moves the counter towards the 20 (adding) and player 2 moves it towards the -20 (subtracting). The winner is the first player to reach their top number.

Order of operations

Lilia is collecting eggs on her parents' farm. She puts 2 eggs in a pan for lunch and fills 5 boxes of 6 eggs to sell. She writes this as 2 + 6 × 5 and asks her brother to work out how many she has collected in total. He says it's 40 eggs but Lilia isn't sure. She thinks it's 32 eggs. Who is correct and why?

....

....

The next day, Lilia collects 41 eggs and puts them in 3 boxes of 12. Which of these calculations shows how many eggs she has left?

$$12 \times 3 - 41 \qquad 41 - 12 \div 3$$

$$41 - 12 \times 3 \qquad 41 \div 12 - 3$$

These are the calculations Lilia writes for the eggs she collects on the remaining five days of the week. Circle the calculations she has done correctly according to BIDMAS. What should each answer have been?

$$3 + 8 \times 4 = 44$$

$$52 - 4 \times 5 = 32$$

$$60 + 12 \div 6 = 12$$

$$12 \times 5 - 3 = 24$$

$$30 - 4 \times 6 = 6$$

....

....

....

....

....

Answers on page 128

PARENT TIP: The rule of **BIDMAS** helps us work out the answer to a multi-step calculation by following the order: **B**rackets **I**ndices **D**ivision **M**ultiplication **A**ddition **S**ubtraction. Throw a dice three times. Using the numbers in any order, how many different answers can your child make using the rules of BIDMAS?

Factors and multiples

Bobby and Georgina are at the skate park on neighbouring ramps. Bobby stops for a rest at the top of the ramp after every 3 half pipes. Georgina stops after every 4 half pipes.

After how many half pipes will they both stop at the same time for the first time?

....

When will be the next three times that both of them will stop for a rest together?

....

Will they both stop together after 130 half pipes? How do you know?

....

....

Josh and Charlotte arrive at the skate park. They set off together but stop to rest at different times. They both stop for a rest together after 18 half pipes and then again after 36. After how many half pipes were they stopping to rest?

....

Bobby has brought 17 sweets with him that he wants to share but can't seem to divide them equally with his friends. Can you explain to Bobby why it isn't possible to share his sweets equally with anyone?

....

....

Can you think of three other numbers of sweets, less than 30, which can't be shared equally?

....

Answers on page 128

PARENT TIP: Play Times Tables Aerobics with your child. Pick two or more times tables and choose an action to represent multiples of each number, e.g. raise right arm for multiples of 3, or jump for multiples of 4. Count aloud from 1 and perform the actions when you say a multiple of the chosen times tables. How high can you count before you make a mistake?

Calculating mentally

Miss Appleby's class is having a maths quiz. The children must solve each calculation mentally with jottings. Alfie has done one question from each round. Use his examples to help you solve the other calculations.

Round 1
Rounding and adjusting

Alfie's workings out:
234 + 19 = 234 + 20 −1 = 253

1. £13.46 + £2.99

....

2. 4650 − 1990

....

Round 2
Double one number and halve the other

Alfie's workings out:
13 × 4 = 26 × 2 = 52

1. 18 × 5

....

2. 24 × 6

....

Round 3
Factorising and reordering

Alfie's workings out:
14 × 12 = 7 × 2 × 12 = 84 × 2 = 168

1. 16 × 5

2. 24 × 8

....

Answers on page 128

PARENT TIP: Encourage your child to calculate mentally before using a written method. Ask them to consider: Can I use doubling or halving? Can I use the times tables that I know? Can I round the number and adjust the answer? Your child's recall of number bonds is crucial to their ability to calculate mentally.

Round 4
Partitioning and recombining

Alfie's workings out:
$18 \times 3 = 10 \times 3 + 8 \times 3 = 30 + 24 = 54$

1. 23×5

2. 17×6

3. 32×7

4. 26×8

Round 5
Using known facts

Alfie's workings out:
$3.2 \div 4 = 0.8$ because $32 \div 4 = 8$

1. 1.2×3

2. $6.3 \div 9$

3. $540 \div 6$

4. $280 \div 7$

Answers on page 128

Multiplying: written methods

The Mathemagical Theme Park has a different ticket price each day depending on how busy it expects to be. These are the admission numbers and ticket prices for each day of half term.

day	ticket price	admissions
Monday	£24	236
Tuesday	£18	304
Wednesday	£21	187
Thursday	£29	245
Friday	£32	453

Can you work out the total money taken for tickets each day? The first one is done for you.

Monday	Tuesday	Wednesday	Thursday	Friday
236	304	187	245	453
× 24	× 18	× 21	× 29	× 32
944				
+ 4720				
£5664				

ⓐ Which day made the most money? ....

ⓑ Here is the calculation for Saturday's admissions. Can you write the missing numbers?

Saturday

$$
\begin{array}{r}
5 \bigcirc 3 \\
\times \quad \bigcirc 5 \\
\hline
2\ 7\ 1\ \bigcirc \\
+\ \bigcirc 6\ 2\ 9\ 0 \\
\hline
£1\ \bigcirc 0\ \bigcirc 5
\end{array}
$$

ⓒ The manager has worked out the takings for Sunday but has made a mistake. Can you explain it?

Sunday

$$
\begin{array}{r}
628 \\
\times \quad 38 \\
\hline
5024 \\
+\ 1884 \\
\hline
£6908
\end{array}
$$

....

....

Answers on page 128

Multiplying decimals

(a) A group of friends stop at a café for lunch. 3 of them decide to get pizza which costs £7.85 each and the other 5 have burgers at £5.49 each. What do they spend more on, pizza or burgers?

pizza

$$7.85 \times 3$$

£ _____

burgers

$$5.49 \times 5$$

£ _____

(b) The 8 friends each order a fizzy drink which is 0.85 litres. How much does the waitress pour out in total?

fizzy drinks

$$0.85 \times 8$$

_____

litres

(c) The café has some delicious brownies. Each brownie is 12.5cm long and there are 7 brownies left. How long are they in total?

brownies

$$12.5 \times 7$$

_____

cm

Answers on page 128

Answers on page 128

PARENT TIP: Give your child five random digits, e.g. 2, 3, 5, 7, 8. They need to use them to make a 3-digit number and a 2-digit number to multiply, e.g. 537 × 82. What is the largest product they can make? What's the smallest? Repeat with a decimal number with up to two places multiplied by a single digit, e.g. 23.57 × 8.

Dividing: written methods

At the Arty Electronics factory, video game consoles are being packed into boxes, ready to send to the shops. The iBot is packed in boxes of 15, the SpaceBlast in boxes of 24 and the Gamezone in boxes of 32.

This week, 3845 iBots, 6196 SpaceBlasts and 4272 Gamezones were made.

How many boxes will be filled with each video game console and how many of each will be left unboxed?

$$15 \overline{\smash{)}3845} \qquad 24 \overline{\smash{)}6196} \qquad 32 \overline{\smash{)}4272}$$

iBots left unboxed	SpaceBlasts left unboxed	Gamezones left unboxed
....	....	....

The following week, Rory, one of the factory workers, has worked out that he will need 124 boxes for 1876 iBots. What mistake has he made?

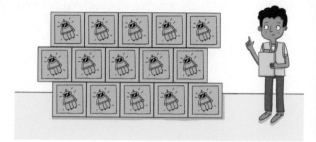

Rory's workings out:

$$15 \overline{\smash{)}18\overset{3}{7}\overset{7}{6}} \quad {}^{124 \ r16}$$

....
....
....
....
....
....

Answers on page 128

939 SpaceBlasts were sold in the last 7 days. How many is that each day? Round your answer to one decimal place.

$$7 \sqrt{939}$$

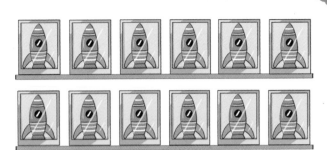

The special offer shelf is 195cm long. 6 Gamezones fit side by side on the shelf. How long is the Gamezone's box?

$$\sqrt{}$$

Two rival shops sold the Gamezone at different prices. Game World sold 25 for a total of £5990 and Gaming First sold 16 for a total of £4020. Which shop sold the Gamezone console for the highest price?

$$\sqrt{}$$

$$\sqrt{}$$

In one shop, 28 iBots were sold in the first week, making a total of £5313. How much did each one sell for?

$$\sqrt{}$$

Answers on page 128

PARENT TIP: Encourage your child to make a list of multiples of the number they are dividing by at the side of the calculation. Counting aloud in multiples of numbers they are less familiar with will help with this, e.g. 23, 46, 69, 92. Try taking turns to count the different multiples.

Ordering fractions

After the Year 6 cake sale at school, there is enough cake left for a second cake sale. These are the fractions of each cake left over.

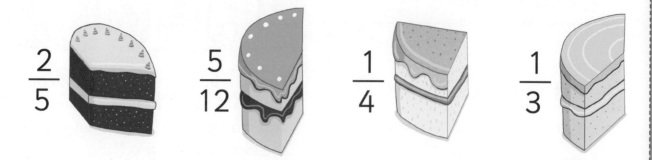

$\frac{2}{5}$ $\frac{5}{12}$ $\frac{1}{4}$ $\frac{1}{3}$

Using equivalent fractions, put the cake stickers from the sticker sheet in order of what is left, starting with the smallest fraction and ending with the biggest.

Mia's chocolate cake was cut into 12 pieces. There is less than $\frac{1}{2}$ but more than $\frac{1}{3}$ left at the end of the cake sale. Orla's toffee cake was cut into 8 pieces. There is more than $\frac{1}{2}$ but less than $\frac{3}{4}$ left. Use the stickers on your sticker sheet and stick in the fraction of each girl's cake that is left.

Mia's
chocolate cake

Orla's
toffee cake

Mia says they have the same amount of cake left, but Orla disagrees. Who is correct and why?

....

....

....

Answers on page 128

Adding and subtracting fractions

Some children brought the same types of cakes, so the next day, Mr Nelson combines these cakes together for the second cake sale.

Joe's mum made two carrot cakes for the sale. One was cut into 10 equal pieces and the other into 8. There are 3 pieces of each cake left for the second sale. What fraction is left altogether?

$$\frac{3}{10} + \frac{3}{8} =$$

There were $2\frac{1}{2}$ chocolate cakes at the first cake sale. At the end of the sale only $\frac{4}{5}$ of one cake is left. What fraction was sold?

Ethan made three Victoria sponge cakes with his dad for the first sale. At the end, $\frac{1}{4}$, $\frac{2}{3}$ and $\frac{3}{8}$ of the cakes are left. How much is there altogether for the second sale?

Answers on page 128

PARENT TIP: Give your child the opportunity to cut up cakes, pizza and other food into equal parts. Can they describe the fraction? Ask them how they could change a fraction cut into quarters so it is cut into eighths. What will they have to do to each piece? What other fractions could they turn the pieces into?

Multiplying fractions

Dan is the project manager of a new house that is being built. This is how the plot of land will be divided up:

house: $\frac{3}{5}$ garden: $\frac{1}{4}$ driveway: $\frac{1}{10}$ garage: $\frac{1}{20}$

Dan does some calculations to work out the fraction of the whole site that different features will take up. Can you help him find the answers?

The lounge is $\frac{1}{4}$ of the house.

$$\frac{1}{4} \times \frac{3}{5} =$$

The shed is $\frac{1}{8}$ of the garden.

$$\frac{1}{8} \times \frac{1}{4} =$$

Dan has got dirt on one of his calculations. Place the missing number stickers 3, 5, 6 and 10 in the correct places in the calculation:

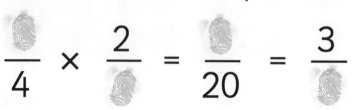   

$$\frac{}{4} \times \frac{2}{} = \frac{}{20} = \frac{3}{}$$

The builders are ready to start building the house. $\frac{1}{3}$ of the bricks have been delivered, but $\frac{1}{2}$ of them are damaged. What fraction of the total bricks are ready for the builders to use?

....

....

$\frac{3}{5}$ of the doors need to be fitted by the end of the day. Nisha the joiner has to fit $\frac{3}{4}$ of them. What fraction of all the doors will she fit?

....

....

Answers on page 128

Dividing fractions

Dan has asked the tilers to start work on the kitchen. $\frac{2}{5}$ of the tiles are patterned. These will be split equally between the windowsill and sink. What fraction of the tiles will be used on the windowsill?

$$\frac{2}{5} \div 2 =$$

Can you help Dan to work out how much of each of these other materials to put in each room?

$\frac{2}{3}$ of all the timber is needed to build identical wardrobes in the 4 bedrooms. What fraction of all the timber should go in each room?

....

....

$\frac{1}{5}$ of the bags of plaster will be used in the 2 bathrooms. What fraction of the bags should Dan take to each bathroom?

....

....

$\frac{3}{8}$ of the insulation panels will be used in the 6 rooms upstairs. What fraction of the panels should be taken to each room?

....

....

Answers on page 128

PARENT TIP: Throw a dice four times to make the numerators and the denominators of two proper fractions, e.g. $\frac{2}{5}$ and $\frac{1}{2}$. Take turns to find their product. Who can make the largest fraction each time?

113

Fractions, decimals, percentages

Three sales assistants in a department store are putting sale tickets on some clothes. They do it in three different ways.

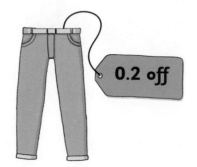

0.2 off

15% off

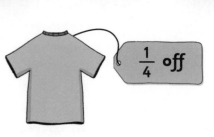

$\frac{1}{4}$ off

Which item of clothing has the most off? Explain why.

the t-shirt because it is a quarter

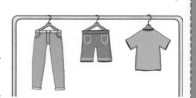

Match the sales tickets that show the same discount.
One has been done for you.

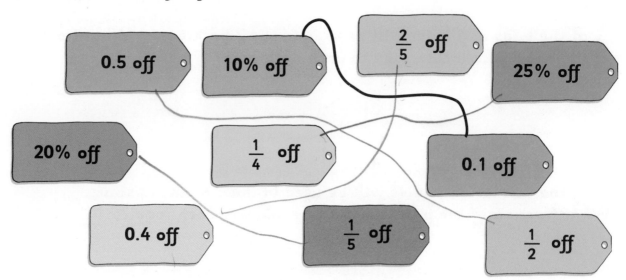

0.5 off 10% off $\frac{2}{5}$ off 25% off

20% off $\frac{1}{4}$ off 0.1 off

0.4 off $\frac{1}{5}$ off $\frac{1}{2}$ off

Anna has written all her sales tickets as percentages but Matt tells her to change them to fractions in their simplest form. Can you help?

15% off $= \frac{15}{100} \quad \frac{3}{20}$

75% off $= \frac{3}{4}$

60% off $= \frac{2}{5}$

114

Answers on page 128

Percentages

Pacha and his mum are in the sportswear department, choosing a new football kit. Calculate the savings on these football shirts.

£30   20% off

£42   30% off

£28   15% off

Saving of ....   Saving of ....   Saving of ....

A pair of football boots has 40% off. Pacha says he has two different ways to calculate this.

	Method 1: find 10% and multiple by 4.	Method 2: find 50% and subtract 10%.
a) £24	....	....
b) £60	....	....
c) £80	....	....

Which method do you prefer?

....

....

Pacha wants a pair of boots that cost £60 but today there's 30% off.
He says, "You just divide by 3 so the saving is £20."
His mum disagrees. Can you explain to him why he is wrong?

....

....

Answers on page 128

PARENT TIP: Play Would You Rather? with your child. Give your child real amounts to choose between, e.g. would you rather have 20% of 40 minutes on your tablet or 25% of 60 minutes? Would you rather have 30% of 20 grapes or 90% of 10 grapes?

Ratios

These are the numbers of different animals that came into the vet's surgery on Monday.

type of animal	number
dogs	12
cats	8
rabbits	3
hamsters	4
snakes	1
birds	2

Write these ratios in their simplest form.

dogs : hamsters ....

cats : birds ....

snakes : rabbits ....

These are the ratios of animals that came to see the vet on Tuesday.

cats : rabbits	dogs : rabbits	dogs : hamsters
5 : 1	4 : 1	3 : 2

The vet treated 15 cats. Complete this table to show how many of each animal was treated.

type of animal	number treated
dogs	
cats	15
rabbits	
hamsters	

Answers on page 128

On Wednesday, the vet saw 2 dogs for every 1 cat that came in for treatment. The vet treated 6 cats. How many dogs did she see?

....

....

Snakes and rabbits were brought in on Friday in the ratio of 1 snake for every 3 rabbits. There were 9 rabbits. How many snakes were brought in?

....

....

On Saturday, rabbits, hamsters and birds came to see the vet in the ratio 3:2:1. There were 24 rabbits, hamsters and birds in total. How many of each animal was there?

....

....

On Saturday and Sunday, the vet examined dogs in the ratio 2:3. If she examined 8 dogs on Saturday, how many did she examine on Sunday?

....

....

The vet saw 15 cats on Saturday and 18 cats on Sunday. She says the ratio of cats on Saturday compared to Sunday was 6:5. Is she right?

....

....

Answers on page 128

PARENT TIP: Give your child a chance to think about ratio in everyday life, e.g. a recipe may ask for 200g of flour for every 1 egg, so if you use 600g of flour, how many eggs do you need? Ratio is also used when diluting cordial, e.g. 100ml of cordial for every 900ml of water. This is 1:9 in its simplest form.

Algebra

Cooper is the manager at the mobile phone shop and has given his employees a formula for working out how much customers will pay each month (c) for each different tariff based on how much data (d) they use.

Can you write out the formula for each phone tariff? The first formula has been done for you.

tariff 1
£25 per month plus £3 per GB of data

c = 25 + 3d

tariff 2
£34 per month plus £2 per GB of data

....

tariff 3
£21 per month plus £5 per GB of data

....

tariff 4
£32 per month plus £1.50 per GB of data

....

Emma uses 3GB of data every month. Which is the cheapest tariff for Emma?

....

Using the stickers on the sticker sheet, match each of Emma's friends to the phone tariff that would be cheapest for them.

Ellie uses 10GB of data

Zoe uses 6GB of data

Tabby uses 1GB of data

Answers on page 128

These phones have different tariffs for customers who want to pay as they go for calls (m) and texts (t) only.

Write a formula for each phone tariff. The first one is done for you.

Mobile 1

50p per minute
plus 3p per text

$c = 50m + 3t$

Mobile 2

20p per minute
plus 5p per text

....

Mobile 3

10p per minute
plus 20p per text

....

Mobile 4

30p per minute
plus 10p per text

....

Sid is helping his grandmother choose a phone. He estimates that she will use about 300 minutes and 100 texts a month. Which phone should she buy and how much would she pay?

....

....

At the end of the first month, Sid's grandmother actually used about 200 minutes and 200 texts. Did they make the right decision and why?

....

....

Answers on page 128

PARENT TIP: Make solving equations fun! Give your child an equation, e.g. 2n + 3. Write the numbers from 0–9 with a pen on an inflatable ball and take turns to throw it back and forth. Whichever number your right thumb lands near becomes the value for n. Put this value into the equation and work out the answer.

Shape

Sinead loves making presents for her friends. She has built these gift boxes from nets she printed out from the internet. Can you match the net sticker from the sticker sheet to the gift box it made?

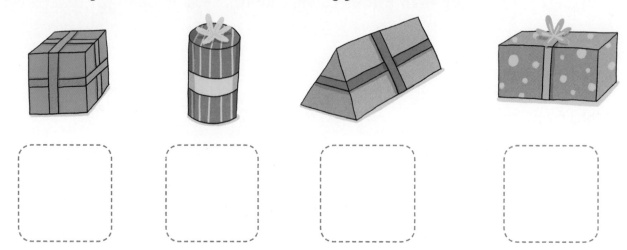

She needs to make a hexagonal prism shaped box for another gift but can't find a net on the internet. She knows it will need hexagonal and rectangular faces. Can you work out how many it will need of each?

hexagonal faces: rectangular faces:

What shapes and how many of each will she need for a pentagonal-based pyramid box?

....

....

Can you draw the net for her in this space?

Answers on page 128

Sinead has been learning about shapes in school and decides to impress her little brother with her 'psychic' powers! She prints off some shapes from the internet. Then she asks him to measure just one angle with his protractor and tells him that she can guess the rest of the shape's angles!

Sinead uses her knowledge of shapes and these two rules:
Angles of a triangle add up to 180°
Angles of a quadrilateral add up to 360°

These are the angles her brother measures on each shape:
Fill in the missing angles that Sinead gives her brother for each shape.

equilateral triangle	isosceles triangle	isosceles trapezium	rhombus

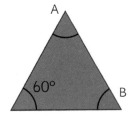

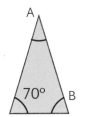

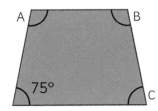

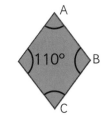

A .... A .... A .... A ....

B .... B .... B .... B ....

                                          C .... C ....

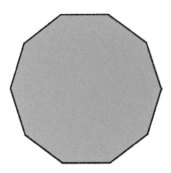

Sinead's dad shows her a rule for the internal angles of regular polygons. He says, "Divide 360° by the number of vertices and subtract that amount from 180°."

Can you use his rule to work out the internal angles of a regular decagon (10-sided shape)?

....

....

Answers on page 128

PARENT TIP: Play My Secret Shape with your child. Take turns to describe a shape using its properties and ask each other to guess it. Use properties, such as lines of symmetry, number of equal sides, angles, 2D or 3D, etc. Also use the angle rules for triangles and quadrilaterals, and ask your child to guess the missing angles in your secret shape.

Converting measures

John and his family are travelling around America during the summer holidays. John has been learning about converting measures in school, so he looks out for measures he can convert along the way.

John keeps track of how far they have driven. How many metres have they travelled each day?

day of the week	distance in km	distance in m
Monday	31.4km	
Tuesday	50.25km	
Wednesday	76.06km	
Thursday	100.5km	
Friday	84.453km	

His dad tells him they have travelled 73 240 metres since they set off this morning. How many kilometres have they travelled so far?

....

Tomorrow they have two journeys of 205 320m and 46.3km to make. How far will they travel in total?

....

They weigh their luggage to make sure it isn't too heavy for the plane flight home. The scale shows 18 450g. Their allowance is 20kg. Are they within the allowance? How do you know?

....

At the gas station, they buy 4 drinks that measure 650ml each. How many litres do the drinks add up to in total?

....

Answers on page 128

John's dad normally measures the distance they travel in miles.
John helps him convert the distances from km to miles using this rule:

5 miles = 8 km

Can you use John's rule to match the distances below?

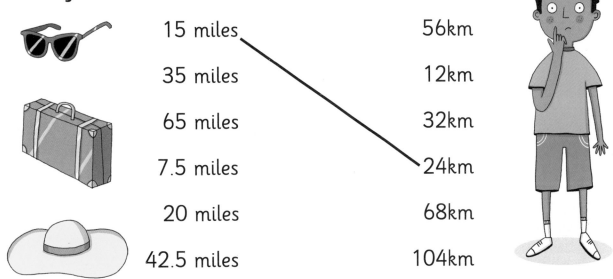

15 miles	56km
35 miles	12km
65 miles	32km
7.5 miles	24km
20 miles	68km
42.5 miles	104km

John's dad says that 1 mile is about 1.6km. Use this rule to complete the boxes with one of these symbols from the sticker sheet:

< > =

2 miles ( ) 4km   1.6 miles ( ) 1km

8 miles ( ) 8km   100 miles ( ) 1000km

10 miles ( ) 16km   160 miles ( ) 16km

Answers on page 128

PARENT TIP: Whenever you drive somewhere, encourage your child to work out the approximate distance in kilometres by using the conversion 5 miles = 8 kilometres. Also you can ask them to use both metric and imperial measures in everyday life, e.g. when you are cooking and the recipe needs 75g of rice, ask your child what it is in kg?

Area and perimeter

Neighbours Kate and Alice are racing each other on their scooters around the outside of their rectangular gardens.

Kate says, "It's not fair because our gardens are different sizes so we won't travel the same distance."

They measure the perimeters to check and are surprised that both perimeters are 44m. What could the length and width of each garden be if they are both whole numbers?

One possibility is 4m by 18m because (4 + 18) × 2 = 44. How many other answers can you find? (Hint: there are 11 possibilities.)

....

....

....

....

Alice says, "The difference between the areas of our gardens is 35m²." What are the measurements of each garden? (Hint: find all possible areas and work out which two have a difference of 35m².)

....

....

....

Answers on page 128

PARENT TIP: Let your child measure the length and width of different rooms and spaces around your home. Which room has the biggest/smallest area? Which has the biggest/smallest perimeter? Is it the same room? Can your child draw another room with the same area but a different perimeter?

In school the next day, Kate and Alice are learning about the area of triangles. Their teacher shows them that if they draw a diagonal across a rectangle they can make two triangles with half the area of the rectangle.

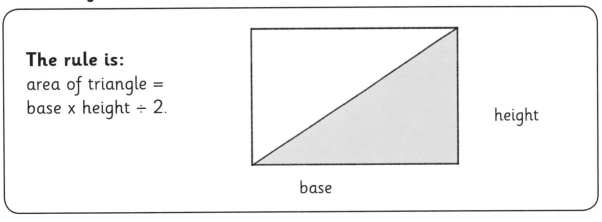

The rule is:
area of triangle =
base x height ÷ 2.

height

base

Can you use the rule to find the area of these triangles?

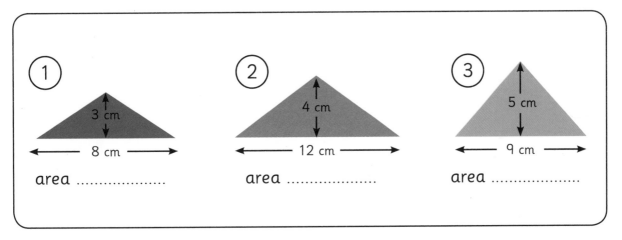

① 3 cm 8 cm
area ....

② 4 cm 12 cm
area ....

③ 5 cm 9 cm
area ....

What are the missing base and height measurements in these triangles?

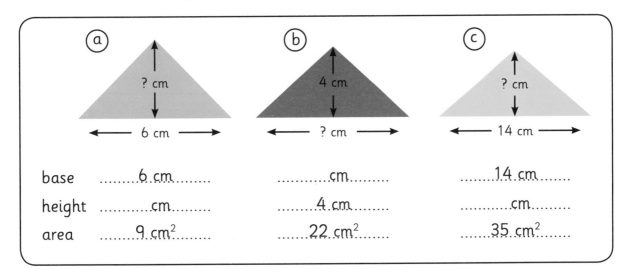

ⓐ ? cm 6 cm

ⓑ 4 cm ? cm

ⓒ ? cm 14 cm

	ⓐ	ⓑ	ⓒ
base	6 cm	.... cm	14 cm
height	.... cm	4 cm	.... cm
area	9 cm²	22 cm²	35 cm²

Answers on page 128

Mean

On Millie's street, the neighbours have been competing to find out who can recycle the most waste. They have kept a record of all the items in their recycling bins over the last few weeks. This is Millie's record:

	plastic bottles	newspapers	tin cans	glass jars
week one	4	2	7	2
week two	6	1	5	4
week three	3	3	9	3
week four	5	4	12	5

Calculate the mean number of each item over the last 4 weeks.

plastic bottles

$(4 + 6 + 3 + 5) \div 4 =$

....

newspapers

....

tin cans

....
....

glass jars

....
....

Tilly next door only recorded her recycling over the last 3 weeks. Can you complete the missing numbers in her table?

	plastic bottles	newspapers	tin cans	glass jars
week one	4		4	10
week two	5	2		11
week three		5	8	
mean	**4**	**3**	**7**	**9**

Answers on page 128

The neighbours compare the number of glass jars they have each recycled. There are 6 houses taking part and they recycled a total of 42 jars. What is the mean number of jars per household?

....

....

Only 3 households recycled tin cans. If their mean number of cans was 6, how many cans did they recycle in total?

....

....

In the last week, only 4 households recycled newspapers. Their mean number of newspapers was 3. If the first 2 households recycled 4 each, how many did the other 2 households recycle?

....

....

The mean number of plastic bottles for 5 households was 4. When the sixth house brings their bottles, the mean increases by 2. How many bottles did the sixth house add to the recycling?

....

....

....

Answers on page 128

PARENT TIP: To find the mean, we add the individual numbers and divide the total by the amount of numbers, e.g. $3 + 6 + 8 + 9 = 26$. There are 4 numbers so $26 \div 4 = 6.5$. Use everyday life situations to help your child practise finding the mean, e.g. you could ask them to work out the mean number of sweets in several paper bags.

Answers

Page 98: Big numbers

Kinsman	Finch	Randles	Hagarth
£8 098 324	£8 235 938	£14 568 400	£15 408 276

player name	wage change	new wages
Randles	£600 000 decrease	£13 968 400
Finch	£70 000 increase	£8 305 938
Kinsman	£450 000 increase	£8 548 324
Hagarth	£9000 decrease	£15 399 276

digits 1 & 2	£2 321 450	<	£2 323 640
digits 2 & 2	£2 322 450	<	£2 323 640
digits 3 & 2	£2 323 450	<	£2 323 640
digits 4 and above & 3 and above	£2 324 450	<	£2 333 640

Page 99: Decimal numbers
No, Robbie is wrong. James should say, "4 tenths is larger than 1 tenth so the rest of the digits don't matter."
William is wrong. 14 003m ÷ 1000 = 14.003km
Robbie: 12.042km   Jenny: 9.802km   William: 10.46km
Poppy: 15.8km   Connor: 8.045km
13.4km × 1000 = 13 400m   3400cm ÷ 100 = 34m

Page 100: Rounding numbers
The black car: £12 549 rounds up to £13 000.
Kyle's dad will pay £15 000.
It is the same price: £15 000.

£14 750   £12 895   £28 434   £18 435

Page 101: Negative numbers
Toronto and London: 20ºC
Toronto and Moscow: 11ºC
London and Moscow: 31ºC
Moscow and Rio: 46ºC
Toronto and Rio: 35ºC
From 9ºC to -9ºC is a difference of 18ºC. It should be 29ºC, 19ºC, 9ºC, -1ºC, -11ºC

Page 102: Order of operations
Lilia is correct. Multiplication comes before addition: (6 × 5) + 2 = 30 + 2 = 32
41 – 12 × 3. Lilia has 5 eggs left.
3 + 8 × 4 = 44 is wrong, the correct answer is 35.
52 × 4 × 5 = 32 is correct.
60 + 12 ÷ 6 = 12 is wrong, the correct answer is 62.
12 × 5 × 3 = 24 is wrong, the correct answer is 57.
30 – 4 × 6 = 6 is correct.

Page 103: Factors and multiples
12 half pipes.
24, 36 and 48 half pipes.
No. 130 isn't a multiple of 12.
They were stopping at 2 and 9 half pipes, or 3 and 6 half pipes.
17 is a prime number and prime numbers can only be divided by itself and 1.
2, 3, 5, 7, 11,13,19, 23, 29 are all prime numbers below 30.

Pages 104–105: Calculating mentally
Round 1:
1. £13.46 + £2.99 = £13.46 + £3 – £0.01 = £16.45
2. 4650 – 1990 = 4650 – 2000 + 10 = 2660
Round 2:
1. 18 × 5 = 9 × 10 = 90
2. 24 × 6 = 12 × 12 = 144
Round 3:
1. 16 × 5 = 4 × 4 × 5 = 4 × 20 = 80
2. 24 × 8 = 12 × 2 × 8 = 96 × 2 = 192
Round 4:
1. 23 × 5 = 20 × 5 + 3 × 5 = 100 + 15 = 115
2. 17 × 6 = 10 × 6 + 7 × 6 = 60 + 42 = 102
3. 32 × 7 = 30 × 7 + 2 × 7 = 210 + 14 = 224
4. 26 × 8 = 20 × 8 + 6 × 8 = 160 + 48 = 208
Round 5:
1. 1.2 × 3 = 3.6 because 12 × 3 = 36
2. 6.3 ÷ 9 = 0.7 because 63 ÷ 9 = 7
3. 540 ÷ 6 = 90 because 54 ÷ 6 = 9
4. 280 ÷ 7 = 40 because 28 ÷ 7 = 4

Page 106: Multiplying: written methods
a. Friday made the most money.

	Monday	Tuesday	Wednesday	Thursday	Friday	b. Saturday
	236	304	187	245	453	543
×	24	18	21	29	32	35
	944	2432	187	2205	906	2715
+	4720	3040	3740	4900	13 590	16 290
	£5664	£5472	£3927	£7105	£14 496	£19 005

c. The manager has forgotten to use a place holder when multiplying by 30.

Page 107: Multiplying decimals
a. The friends spend more on burgers.
b. The waitress pours 6.8 litres in total.
c. The brownies are 87.5cm long.

Pages 108–109: Dividing: written methods
The iBots fill 256 boxes with 5 left unboxed. The SpaceBlasts fill 258 boxes with 4 left unboxed. The Gamezones fill 133 boxes with 16 left unboxed. The answer 125 r1, not 124 r16. You cannot have a remainder of 16 when dividing by 15.
134.1 SpaceBlasts were sold each day.
The Gamezone's box is 32.5cm long.
Gaming First sold the Gamezone at the higher price.
The iBots sold for £189.75 each.

Page 110: Ordering fractions

$\frac{1}{4}$ $\frac{1}{3}$ $\frac{2}{5}$ $\frac{5}{12}$

Mia $\frac{5}{12}$ Orla $\frac{5}{8}$
Orla is correct because even though they both have 5 pieces left, her eighths are bigger than Mia's twelfths.

Page 111: Adding and subtracting fractions
Carrot cakes: $\frac{27}{40}$. Chocolate cakes: $1\frac{7}{10}$. Victoria sponge cakes: $1\frac{7}{24}$.

Page 112: Multiplying fractions
Lounge: $\frac{3}{20}$. Shed: $\frac{1}{32}$. $\frac{3}{4} \times \frac{2}{5} = \frac{6}{20} = \frac{3}{10}$
Bricks: $\frac{1}{6}$. Doors: $\frac{9}{20}$.

Page 113: Dividing fractions
Tiles: $\frac{1}{5}$. Timber: $\frac{1}{6}$. Bags of plaster: $\frac{1}{10}$. Insulation panels: $\frac{1}{16}$.

Page 114: Fractions, decimals, percentages
$\frac{1}{4}$ off is best because it is the same as 0.25 (more than 0.2), or 25% (more than 15%).

0.5 off   10% off $\frac{2}{5}$ off   25% off
20% off $\frac{1}{4}$ off   0.1 off
0.4 off $\frac{1}{5}$ off $\frac{1}{2}$ off

15% = $\frac{15}{100}$ = $\frac{3}{20}$.   75% = $\frac{3}{4}$.   60% = $\frac{3}{5}$.

Page 115: Percentages
Shirt 1: £30 – 20% off saving of £6   Shirt 2: £42 – 30% off saving of £12.60
Shirt 3: £28 – 15% off saving of £4.20
a. method 1: £2.40 × 4 = £9.60   method 2: £12 – £2.40 = £9.60
b. method 1: £6 × 4 = £24   method 2: £30 – £6 = £24
c. method 1: £8 × 4 = £32   method 2: £40 – £8 = £32
30% is 3 × 10%, which is 3 × £6, so £18. Dividing by 3 would be finding $\frac{1}{3}$ which is the same as 33.333...%, not 30%.

Pages 116–117: Ratios
dogs : hamsters = 3:1   cats : birds = 4:1   snakes : rabbits = 1:3

type of animal	number treated
dogs	12
cats	15
rabbits	3
hamsters	8

12 dogs. 3 snakes. 12 rabbits, 8 hamsters and 4 birds. 12 dogs. No, the ratio is 5:6.

Pages 118–119: Algebra
1. [c = 25 + 3d]   2. [c = 34 + 2d]   3. [c = 21 + 5d]   4. [c = 32 + 1.5d]
Mobile tariff 1 is the cheapest for Emma.
Mobile tariff 4 is cheapest for Ellie and Zoe. Mobile tariff 3 is cheapest for Tabby.
1. [c = 50m + 3t]   2. [c = 20m + 5t]   3. [c = 10m + 20t]   4. [c = 30m + 10t]
Sid's grandmother should buy mobile 3 and would pay £50.
No, they should have bought mobile 2, it would have been £10 cheaper.

Pages 120–121: Shape

Pentagonal-based pyramid box net:

2 hexagonal faces and 6 rectangular faces.
1 pentagonal face and 5 triangular faces.

Equilateral triangle	60° and 60°
Isosceles triangle	70° and 40°
Isosceles trapezium	75°, 105° and 105°
Rhombus	110°, 70° and 70°

Decagon internal angle: 180 – (360 ÷ 10) = 144°

Pages 122–123: Converting measures

day of the week	distance in km	distance in m
Monday	31.4km	31 400m
Tuesday	50.25km	50 250m
Wednesday	76.06km	76 060m
Thursday	100.5km	100 500m
Friday	84.453km	84 453m

73.24km. 251.62km (or 251 620m). Yes, 18 450g = 18.45kg. 2.6 litres in total.

[15 miles = 24km   35 miles = 56km   65 miles = 104km   7.5 miles = 12km
20 miles = 32km   42.5 miles = 68km]

2 miles	<	4km	1.6 miles	>	1km
8 miles	>	8km	100 miles	<	1000km
10 miles	=	16km	160 miles	>	16km

Pages 124–125: Area and perimeter
1m by 21m   2m by 20m   3m by 19m   4m by 18m   5m by 17m
6m by 16m   7m by 15m   8m by 14m   9m by 13m   10m by 12m
11m by 11m.
The two gardens must be 5m × 17m = 85m² and 10m × 12m = 120m²
because 120m² – 85m² = 35m²

Triangle 1	8 × 3 ÷ 2 = 12cm²
Triangle 2	12 × 4 ÷ 2 = 24cm²
Triangle 3	9 × 5 ÷ 2 = 22.5cm²

Triangle a	Base = 6cm	Height = 3cm	Area = 9cm²
Triangle b	Base = 11cm	Height = 4cm	Area = 22cm²
Triangle c	Base = 14cm	Height = 5cm	Area = 35cm²

Pages 126–127: Mean
plastic bottles (4 + 6 + 3 + 5) ÷ 4 = 4.5
newspapers   (2 + 1 + 3 + 4) ÷ 4 = 2.5
tin cans   (7 + 5 + 9 + 12) ÷ 4 = 8.25
glass jars   (2 + 4 + 3 + 5) ÷ 4 = 3.5

	plastic bottles	newspapers	tin cans	glass jars
week one	4	2	4	10
week two	5	2	9	11
week three	3	5	8	6
mean	4	3	7	9

7 jars per household. 18 cans in total. 4 between them (1+3 or 2+2). 16 bottles.